Tales of
Old Northumberland

Joan Morgan

With illustrations by Clive Stevens

COUNTRYSIDE BOOKS
NEWBURY, BERKSHIRE

First published in 2006
© Joan Morgan, 2006

COUNTRYSIDE BOOKS
2 HIGHFIELD AVENUE
NEWBURY, BEKSHIRE

To view our complete range of books,
please visit us at
www.countrysidebooks.co.uk

ISBN 1 84674 009 6
EAN 978 184674 009 1

Produced through MRM Associates Ltd., Reading
Typeset by Mac Style, Nafferton, E. Yorkshire
Printed by Woolnough Bookbinding Ltd., Irthlingborough

Contents

For my husband Andy
and my daughter Jane

Introduction

I was born on Tyneside and, apart from two short intervals, I have lived most of my life in Northumberland. To me, Northumberland is the most beautiful and most interesting county in England, and it has been a fascinating experience collecting and researching these stories, which I hope capture the essence of this diverse area.

In addition to the highly populated south-east corner, with its industrial background and its famously friendly outspoken inhabitants, Northumberland covers a huge, sparsely populated stretch of land which displays spectacular beaches, magnificent castles, big skies, lush valleys, wild hills and craggy fells – and at every turn the evidence of a very bloody history. This has never been a place for cissies!

The people of this region have had a lot to put up with since the Romans muscled in and built their great wall. Hundreds of years of border warfare placed them always at the cutting edge of trouble, and the relentless poverty which inevitably followed made 'survival at any cost' the first rule.

The sheer number of castles, bastles and pele towers dotted around the countryside are a constant reminder of this troubled past, and it is easy to imagine gangs of reivers galloping over the sweeping landscape on their nefarious forays, terrorising the poor farming communities.

No wonder, then, that Northumberland has always been awash with strong characters, men and women who were never afraid to fight their corner. Some of these, I have tried to bring back to life in my telling of the stories.

This is my choice of 'Tales of Old Northumberland', and I hope you enjoy reading them as much as I have enjoyed writing them.

Joan Morgan

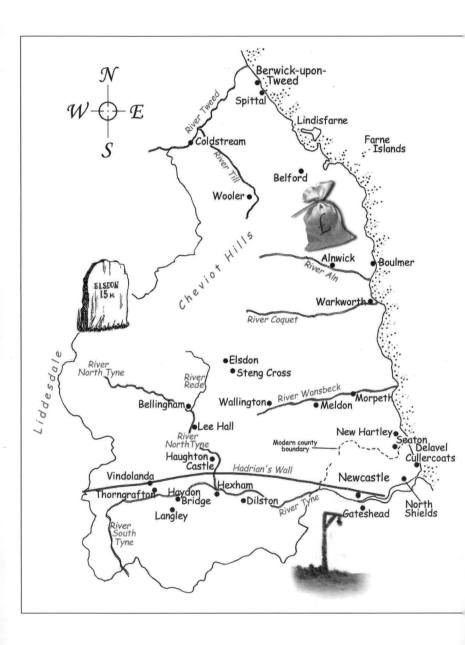

The Long Pack

The year was 1723, and Colonel Ridley took his family away from the cold North Tyne valley to London for the winter – but he was to return sooner than he expected!

The Colonel had amassed a fortune in India during his career with the East India Company. He had retired to his native Northumberland to buy Lee Hall, a large country house on the wooded banks of the Tyne between Wark and Bellingham, and in it he had stored many of his treasures, including a collection of valuable plate worth about £1,000, a vast sum of money in those days. It was the custom among the better-off Northumbrian landowners at the time to spend the winter months in the capital, to enjoy the high-life and to escape the cold, bleak northern climate. So it was that Lee Hall and its valuable treasures were left that winter in the care of three servants; these were Alice, a maid-servant, Richard, an elderly retainer, and Edward, the young farmhand.

Obviously, the Colonel had great faith in his trusted servants. However, he had placed upon them a huge responsibility, especially as this border area, until the unification of the Scottish and English crowns not so very long ago, had suffered three centuries of almost unchecked lawlessness, robbery and violence, and these habits died hard. The tradition of stealing was still rife.

For the three servants, life at Lee Hall soon settled into a routine after the Colonel and his family had departed to London. Until one bitterly cold afternoon, as the light was beginning to fade and Alice was alone in the house, there came a loud rapping at the back door. Her first reaction when she opened it to see a sturdy young pedlar standing there carrying a huge pack was excitement. Life had become very dull and the prospect of hearing the latest gossip from the neighbourhood and of looking at some interesting trinkets was definitely appealing: but she knew she had to turn him away. She had been given strict instructions from the Colonel not to admit anyone into the house.

The pedlar asked for lodgings for the night, saying he was very weary after tramping for miles that day, but no matter how much he turned on the charm and flirted with her, Alice refused. He then asked if he could leave his heavy pack at the house while he went looking elsewhere for lodgings. Alice, being kind-hearted, agreed, and he placed the bulky item carefully over two chairs in the kitchen.

By now it was almost dark and Alice started to light the candles. Something was bothering her about the strange-looking object on the chairs, and she could not help staring at it. The candlelight flickered. Then she felt prickles all over her body as the pack seemed to move. Gasping and wide-eyed with fear, Alice ran out of the back door and across the courtyard to the stables, where Richard was bedding down the horses.

'Richard, come quick, we have a moving pack in the house,' she shouted.

He laughed, 'You're imaginin' things as usual, lass. But howay, we'll gan an' look.' Pulling his muffler close around his weatherbeaten face against the cold, he followed her over to the house.

Edward, meanwhile, was in the fields shooting at rooks to scare them away from the corn with the aid of an ancient military gun. Either his aim was bad or the gun was too old, but he had managed to kill nothing all afternoon. Now the light was fading fast and his long, gangly legs were covered in freezing mud, so he slung the gun over his shoulder and trudged back to the house to see if Alice had put some food out for him in the kitchen. He found her there with Richard, discussing the pack.

The three stared at the strange-looking object that looked like a coffin. Then, it definitely moved. This was a target Edward would not miss! Young, hotheaded and trigger-happy, he pointed his gun at it and pulled the trigger. A terrible scream came from the pack and blood ran out of it, dripping copiously onto the floor. Richard ran up and tore it open. Inside was a man, gasping his last breaths. Four muskets were strapped to his body, a knife was clenched in his hand, and a silver whistle hung around his neck. The upper and lower parts of his body had been encased in two boxes to disguise his shape.

Edward was the first to realise that this was a plot to rob their master, and that the dead man's accomplices would soon raid the house. Scared into action, the three made a plan.

While Richard and Alice secured the house, barring doors and windows, Edward mounted and rode out to summon the aid of the Colonel's tenants. Before long, he had gathered 25 men into the house, armed with 16 guns, including the four muskets. Then they waited, watching from the windows.

THE LONG PACK

Midnight approached with no attack. Then Edward blew the whistle they had found on the body. Within five minutes there was the sound of galloping hooves and a dozen men appeared, now trotting under the stone gateway and clattering into the courtyard. The light of the moon showed that they were armed to the teeth.

It was just possible to see the surprised look on the attackers' faces when Edward shot the leading man; then guns blazed from every window and several men fell off their horses onto the ground. The rest fled, some howling in pain from their wounds.

Edward ventured out with a courageous friend to assess the damage, and they found four dead men lying about the place. Afraid of a further attack, they retreated inside to wait until morning.

During the night, strange noises disturbed them and they were glad when dawn broke. Then the scene that greeted them was met with huge surprise. The four bodies had been spirited away by the robbers, leaving only large sheets of frozen blood on the ground.

Later that morning, news of the attack spread up and down the North Tyne valley and a considerable crowd of people visited the house. It took several days to get a message to Colonel Ridley in London, and for him to return home, but in the meantime men searched over a wide area for the culprits and rewards were offered for information. The body in the pedlar's pack was kept at Lee Hall for inspection for two weeks, but no one could identify it. No man involved in the plot was ever traced.

Colonel Ridley rewarded his three servants well for their bravery and presence of mind. Old Richard remained in the family for the rest of his life, with a good salary, his only duty being to say prayers for the servants every night. Alice was given a generous payment and she married a tobacconist in Hexham. Brave Edward was made the Colonel's head gamekeeper, and afterwards the Colonel bought him a commission in a foot regiment. Edward was subsequently badly wounded and he eventually bought a little farm of his own in the borders, living for many years to tell the tale of the Long Pack.

The pack's corpse was buried in St Cuthbert's churchyard at Bellingham. To the left of the church entrance can be seen the famous Long Pack tombstone, rectangular in shape like a small coffin, with lines carved along its length which some say represent the cords that tied the pack. Is the robber buried there or not? Legend has it that he is, but in reality the tombstone is probably from medieval times. The strange thing is – when you stare at it in the half-light, you could almost swear that it moves ...

The Forgotten Reiver

Battlemented and romantic, Haughton Castle stands on the wooded banks of the North Tyne opposite Barrasford, surrounded by beautiful rolling countryside. Now one of the oldest inhabited castles in Northumberland, this mighty fortress was originally built to withstand constant attack, and it was the scene of a particularly gruesome event, which took place in the early 16th century during the reign of King Henry VIII.

Sporadic warfare between England and Scotland over the previous three hundred years had reduced Northumberland to a virtual wilderness. During this troubled time, settlement had been encouraged by cheap land and low rents in order to form a buffer zone, and the tradition of 'graveland' or 'dead man's land' meant that when a man died, his property was divided between his sons, resulting in a growing population supported by smaller holdings. The land was often poor, suitable only for the growing of a small plot of barley and the grazing of sheep and cattle over a wider common area.

An old saying 'The father to the bough, and the son to the plough' referred to the father finding it necessary to turn to raiding and stealing – or reiving – to feed his family until he ended up on the hanging tree, and the sons dividing his land between them, and eventually suffering the same fate.

The extreme poverty was aggravated by frequent frontier raids, which were actively encouraged by the governments on both sides of the border to wear down the enemy. Families banded together into clans, or 'graynes', for their own protection as 'lifting' from their neighbours became a necessity for survival. Deadly feuds developed between clans, the violence escalating over generations. Strength ruled, both in numbers and in individuals, and the bigger the clan, the more powerful they became. One historian noted: 'Scarce a soul dared to live in Northumberland unless it was near to some castle or walled town.' Robbery, murder and arson were so commonplace that it was almost impossible for anyone to keep the peace.

Sir Thomas Swinburne was Lord of Haughton during the turbulent time of our story. The surrounding landowners and tenants were increasingly complaining to him of raids, arson, blackmail and extortion by the Border Reivers, the worst offenders being one of the largest of the clans, the Armstrongs. Unlike previous Lords of Haughton, notorious bullies who took neighbouring lands by force, Sir Thomas was an honest, dependable man with a caring nature, and he resolved to tackle the problem.

The man in charge of law and order in the area was Lord Dacre, Warden of the Middle March. There were six marches along the length of the border, East, Middle and West on the English side and corresponding marches on the Scottish side, each with its own warden. Lord Dacre and his English counterparts, encouraged by King Henry to lead raids over the border, often made their own alliances with the clans for mutual benefit. Caught between two camps, the resourceful wardens invariably had their own agendas. Although Lord Dacre had begun his career in an attempt to destroy the Armstrong clan, he was soon seduced into colluding with them, the most persuasive factor being Helen Armstrong, known as 'Dark-Eyed Nellie', the beautiful sister of Archie, chief of the Armstrong clan.

Increasingly frustrated with Lord Dacre's failure to carry out his duty of addressing this state of anarchy, Sir Thomas agreed to deliver a petition on behalf of the honest folk of Tynedale to the Lord Chancellor, Cardinal Wolsey, the King's chief minister, who happened to be visiting York at that time, in the autumn of 1520.

Meanwhile, the Armstrongs were preparing for their next raid. One evening at dinner, Archie Armstrong had been presented with a spur on a plate by his wife – a tactful sign that there was no food left and it was time to ride out again. The clan's base was in Liddesdale, where the borders of Northumberland, Cumbria and Scotland merge. This, like much of the border, is a land of heather-clad moor and quaking bogs, stony outcrops and jutting crags, and sweeping wild fell cut across by rushing streams in green wooded valleys; a perfect place for fleeing Border Reivers to hide from their pursuers with their ill-gotten gains.

The men donned their protective leather jackets and steel bonnets, picked up their bows, spears and axes, and set out on their horses which were small, sturdy and fast, with the ability not only to find their way over the difficult terrain, but also to drive the lifted cattle, sheep and horses back home. An old poet recorded:

THE FORGOTTEN REIVER

The freebooters venture both life and limb,
Good wife and bairn and every other thing;
He must do so, or else must starve and die;
For all his lively-hood comes from the enemie.

They travelled light, galloping eastwards across the Northumbrian countryside to steal anything they could carry. This was an ideal moonlit autumn night for a raid and the farmers were on the lookout for trouble. A fire was lit on the top of a stone tower, which meant the reivers had been spotted. Other fires sprang to life in the distance, warning the locals to run from their rudely thatched brushwood and clay houses with whatever they could carry and take to hills and trees. Those lucky enough to have pele towers or bastles, fortified farmhouses, drove their most precious livestock into the ground floor, and then they climbed up to the first floor and locked themselves and their families in. The element of surprise had gone, but the Armstrongs galloped on towards Tynedale.

A few of Sir Thomas's tenants had been prepared for a raid, and, having been warned by the fires, they lay in wait near some cattle, hoping that the reivers would pass their way. They were not disappointed. With great whoops and howls, they surprised the raiders who, preferring stealth to confrontation, galloped off, not realising that one of their number had been pulled off his horse and, winded, lay pinned to the ground. It was only after the brave tenants had tied up and delivered the reiver to Sir Thomas at the castle that they discovered the identity of their prisoner. They had captured the notorious Archie Armstrong.

Sir Thomas was due to leave for York early the next morning. Although he was delighted at the chief's capture, he knew that a new leader would have already taken Archie's place. Without much further thought, he had the prisoner thrown into the Haughton Castle dungeon, and prepared for his journey.

Accompanied by two local landowners, Sir Thomas rode for three days over rutted tracks and badly pitted roads to reach York. It was only when finally relaxing at his destination that he realised, to his great shock and consternation, that on his girdle hung the only key to the hatch door of the dungeon where Archie Armstrong languished without food or water. He knew that none of the castle servants would dare break down the door, and the prisoner's only hope of survival lay in his hands. A man of conscience, he had no choice but to delegate his mission to his two subordinates and immediately return home with the key.

He rushed to purchase a fresh mount, and rode homewards as fast as the horse would carry him. So relentlessly did he ride that this unfortunate horse dropped dead at Durham. It is said that he rode a further two horses to exhaustion before, exhausted himself, he reached Haughton. 'The prisoner!' he shouted as he dashed into the castle. A torch was brought and he ran to the dungeon. On opening the hatch his worst fears were realised. Archie Armstrong lay dead on the floor: in his extreme hunger and desperation he had gnawed the flesh from his own arms and there was an expression of horror on his face so awful that the observers had to look away.

It is said that after the event the spirit of Archie Armstrong haunted the dungeon with terrible cries that echoed through the castle, and servants were terrified to work there. Eventually the priest of nearby Simonburn was called to exorcise the ghost. All was quiet while the bible that was used in the exorcism remained at the castle, but when it was removed for re-binding the cries recommenced. Only when the bible was restored to the castle did the spirit rest.

Some years after Archie's death, in 1542, the Armstrongs battered down the walls of Haughton Castle and gained an entrance with scaling-ladders; and so the raids and deadly feuds continued until the end of the century, when the castle was almost completely dismantled before being rebuilt and restored. Border conflict gradually ceased at the turn of the century after the union of the crowns, and with growing prosperity, the violent times of the Border Reivers became a thing of the past.

The wild landscape and wide vistas of Northumberland, often bleak but always breathtakingly beautiful, and still dotted liberally with fortified farmhouses and pele towers, make it easy to imagine the days when the Border Reivers, or mosstroopers as they were later known, terrorised the populace. Although uncouth and brutalised through poverty, there is no denying their bravery, resilience and will to survive against all odds. Many of the clan names of the past, including the Armstrongs, still survive in Northumberland, and we can safely say that, unlike the unfortunate Archie in the dungeon of Haughton Castle, the Border Reivers will never be forgotten.

Cuddy Alder's Goose Pies

The tough, bull-necked Tyneside keelmen were a race unique in Northern history. Their name originated from the Anglo-Saxon word *ceol*, which referred to the ancient coracle from which the broad-beamed, big-bellied keelboat was descended.

Proudly the keelmen dressed in their peculiar uniform of tall hat, blue jacket, short flannel 'drawers' and blue worsted stockings. Their job was to convey loads of coal from collection points upriver and transport them down to the collier brigs that waited inside the harbour bar at Shields. Considerable navigation skills were required to negotiate their craft through the shingly shallows of the River Tyne; but, notorious for their hard-drinking, hard-swearing ways, and swaggeringly boastful of their physical prowess, the keelmen were often the butt of jokes suggesting their lack of brainpower.

The 'black diamond' coal made the North East increasingly prosperous, a state of affairs that mainly benefited the coal owners and the shipping merchants. The keelmen were paid by the load, which depended on the buoyancy of the river trade. Several times in the early 18th century, during particularly lean times, they went on strike to improve their lot, and they were noted for taking their struggle to the point of starvation before yielding.

In the autumn of 1709 most of the 1,600 keelmen on the Tyne undertook a 'rebellion of the belly'. Food became so scarce on the Sandgate, the shambolic streets on the quayside where most of the keelmen lived, that whole families were on the brink of starvation. The rivermen took to thieving wherever they could.

Not long before Christmas, Geordie, a strapping young keelman, walked to the outskirts of Newcastle to look for odd jobs. He came to a big house at Low Weetslade, near Longbenton and, as he trudged up to the back entrance, he bumped into the owner, an elderly gentleman named Cuthbert Alder. The man had no work for Geordie, but, taking pity on him, he sent him into the kitchen for some refreshment.

The eyes in the hungry young man's face bulged out of his head as he caught sight of the larder, stocked full of wonderful dishes ready for the festive season. He was given a slice of goose pie, which was so marvellously tasty it was easily the best thing he had ever eaten.

In the following days, Geordie could not stop thinking of those goose pies. The memory of them made his mouth drool. He was even dreaming about them. Before long his friends were also drawn into the fantasy of the pies. They had to do something about it. They had to raid Mr Alder's larder.

One frosty, moonlit night soon afterwards, a gang of six hungry young men set out for Mr Alder's house. It was in a secluded situation, so they thought the old man would be a pushover.

However, events did not go completely their way. They first had to scare off a group of travelling tailors who were lodging in the house. Then Mr Alder himself put up a very brave fight – but it was the Amazonian housekeeper who was the most violent adversary. She fought the astonished keelmen with every utensil and item of furniture she could lay her hands on. Valiantly she threw herself into battle to protect the larder, until, finally, she had to retire from the scene with a broken arm.

The keelmen were so exasperated by the defence of the food that some of them elected to kill Mr Alder, who refused to give up. Geordie, however, remembering the man's kindness and, feeling a stab of conscience, stepped in and prevented them. Instead, he urged, they should fill their sacks with the goose pies, and anything else they could lay their hands on, and make themselves scarce before the sleeping servants appeared from the outhouses.

In the following weeks, all attempts to find the plunderers failed, and the offered reward money remained unclaimed. Then Mr Alder himself found a clue. He received some change in silver one day at a shop on Newcastle quayside, and he recognised one of the coins, with a distinctive mark on it, as having been one stolen from his house. Enquiries and discoveries were made, and the guilty keelmen were apprehended, tried, sentenced and jailed.

Geordie, together with one of the gang who had broken the housekeeper's arm and threatened Mr Alder, were publicly hanged upon a gallows erected specially for the occasion on Newcastle Town Moor; the first executions to be held there for 30 years.

For generations afterwards, the keelmen were ridiculed about the 'Raid on the Low Weetslade Larder'. The taunt 'Who'd d'ye like [How did you like] Cuddy Alder's gyuse pies?' would cause fists to fly and noses to be broken.

* * * * * * * * * * * * * *

After the strike was over, in the early spring of 1710, another robbery would be the cause of much hilarity at the keelmen's expense. Many lambs had been mysteriously disappearing from Tyneside farms. The farmers were baffled.

One day, a farmer was crossing his field beside the river. He was absently watching a set of blunt-nosed keelboats, each with its square brown sail catching the weak breeze, making their way slowly down to the sea. Then, to his astonishment, he heard the bleating of a lamb coming from one of the boats.

Quickly, he summoned his labourers, who took to the water. They managed to catch up with the boats, boarded them, and found a live lamb in the huddock (cabin) of one of the keels.

'Hev ye onny lamb in yor huddock?' was the irresistible question that caused many a fight between watermen and landsmen for many years afterwards.

* * * * * * * * * * * * * *

By the year 1880 the keelmen were almost gone. The river had been dredged and improved, and the new steamships were able to reach the coal loading points, making the keels redundant. One of the last surviving keelmen, who retired in the 1860s, remarked, 'Aye mistor, it's them steamers that's brust up the keelmen. It's a bonny bad job, but it cannot be helped.'

Meg
of the
Moneybags

What could a girl do in the late 16th century if she was as plain as a barn door and she had the personality of an abacus? Well, if her daddy was rich, she stood a chance of not ending up an old maid.

Margaret (Meg) Selby was the daughter of Will Selby, a wealthy and some would say miserly and unscrupulous moneylender from Newcastle upon Tyne; others gave him the benefit of the doubt and called him shrewd. Despite his fortune and, in his increasing desperation to marry off his unprepossessing daughter, his willingness to part with a large portion of it, no one would consent to marry the wretched girl. Until, that was, Sir William Fenwick of Wallington, a widower in need of cash, decided to take the plunge and ask for Meg's hand in return for a handsome dowry.

Sir William was undoubtedly a good catch for a moneylender's daughter, giving her through marriage the title of Lady Margaret Fenwick. The 'Fearless Fenwicks' were a powerful clan in Northumberland, famed for their hospitality as well as their valour in battle during the lawless days while England was at war with Scotland. The war was coming to an end and the border raids had just about ceased when Meg married Sir William in 1594, and the Fenwicks could no longer ride out from their family seat at Wallington to take cattle and goods from their northern neighbours. Times were changing, and they had to settle down and make their estates work for them.

Wallington Hall today is a beautiful house owned by the National Trust, with a Palladian façade, clock tower and interior Italian rococo plasterwork, all set in fabulous landscaped gardens sloping down to the River Wansbeck. But when Sir William took his bride there after the wedding, Meg saw a stark house built around a pele tower that had been a fortified refuge for the Fenwick clan in the previous violent years. Inside, where there are now elegant staircases, ladders led from each corner of the reed-strewn great hall up to an open-plan, draughty and comfortless first floor. Meg would not be impressed after her comfortable Newcastle home, but she did her wifely duty over the following years by bearing seven children, and watching her husband spend the money that she had brought to the house with her marriage settlement.

Included in Meg's dowry was a large mortgage on the Meldon estate, five miles to the east of Wallington on the road to Morpeth. Meldon was the inheritance of a popular, carefree young spendthrift who enjoyed life to the full. Consequently, he was hopelessly in debt, and he found it increasingly hard to keep up the large mortgage payments to Sir William.

Sir William died in 1613 at the age of 63. Meg was much younger, only in her late thirties. For most of her married life she had been busy having children, so his death left her the freedom to run her affairs as she chose, and she began to exploit the shrewd nature she had inherited from her father. She foreclosed the Meldon mortgage, effectively excluding the young man from his inheritance, and proceeded to take an active part in managing and running the property, which included Meldon Manor and 460 acres of good farming land.

Meg started to enjoy her new role. She proved to be a capable, ruthless but thoroughly good farmer and estate manager. She went to the markets herself to buy cattle, and she kept an increasingly knowledgeable eye on the crops, quickly becoming an expert agriculturist. As she grew older and richer, she became obsessed with money. Renowned for her greed and her unsympathetic attitude to the less fortunate peasants on her estate, she earned for herself the reputation of being miserly, and behind her back people started to call her 'Meg of the Moneybags'.

Meg had inherited over 30 large properties in the locality. One of these was the modestly sized Hartington Hall, a couple of miles to the north of Wallington, and she increasingly spent her time there, dreaming up ways of safeguarding her money, believing that everyone wanted to rob her, even her most loyal servants. Rumours spread that she was a witch, and that she had a secret underground tunnel between Hartington and Meldon, through which she could hurtle to and fro unseen to conduct private business. This was of course impossible due to the distance of several miles, but there are many holes and crevices in the rock faces of the banks on the River Wansbeck, which could be thought to be the entrances to non-existent passages.

The more riches Meg obtained, the more she felt compelled to hide them away. She hoarded her wealth in the form of gold coins and easily-transported jewels and precious stones, and she wandered around constantly searching for safe hiding places for her treasures.

When Meg died, she was buried at Newminster Abbey, on the outskirts of Morpeth. Soon afterwards, people reported seeing her ghost sitting on a stone trough by the gothic archway in the graveyard. Increasingly, there were stories of her assuming various spectral guises, among them that of a black dog seen crossing the old Meldon Bridge. Her restless spirit was to live on, said to be doomed to wander from hoard to hoard for seven years, then, after resting for the next seven years, to begin the weary round again until all her treasure was found and distributed amongst the poor.

Near the south-east tower of Meldon there was an ancient well down which Meg had reputedly lowered and hidden a bullock's hide pouch stuffed with gold coins. After her death, there was a tale that a local peasant worker had a dream in which he saw Meg by the well, telling him to retrieve the treasure, the only condition being that he must not utter a word from leaving his house to returning to it again with the money. The next night at midnight, he excitedly set out on his own, equipped with chains and a grappling hook. He fished the depths of the well and hauled up the heavy bundle, then, just as it reached the top, he forgot the conditions and cried out, 'There! All the devils alive can't help me getting it now.' At that instant, the chain broke and the bull's hide burst to release its contents back down into the depths of the well, never to be found again.

Another of Meg's secret hiding places was in the roof of a house, then a strong, substantial building, which eventually became Meldon School. At the end of the 19th century, some schoolboys were playing a boisterous game when the ceiling collapsed, and along with the debris a bag fell down onto the floor, bursting open and scattering gold and silver coins at their feet. By the time the schoolmaster came in to investigate, the youngsters were scrambling about for their share of the treasure.

Eventually, all the hiding places, found to be in churches, halls, stables and even under gravestones, were revealed, and except for the one that slipped through the fingers of the peasant in the now dismantled Meldon Well, all the hoards were duly distributed. At last Meg's spirit was said to be able to rest.

Meg was distantly related to the Delavals (see Chapter 16), and the picture gallery at Seaton Delaval Hall used to have an old oil painting of Lady Margaret Fenwick, showing her wearing a stiff silk gown, a heavy ruff, and a broad Dutch type hat tied down at the sides over her ears. Her face looked plain, but her eyes showed a penetrating gaze of superior intelligence and strength of mind.

Was this lady really as bad as she was portrayed? Or was she just a woman lacking the attributes that females were generally admired for, being unforgivably successful in what was considered to be a man's world? Of her seven children, five were girls, and they all married very well, no doubt helped along with huge dowries at massive expense to the widowed Meg. Her sons, Sir William Fenwick of Meldon and Roger of Shortflatt, were both successful men, and there can be no doubt that Meg left them and their estates much richer than they would otherwise have been.

Whatever the truth, her talent for making money in the end may have destroyed her peace of mind, but it also immortalised her, so that instead of dying a plain, forgettable woman of no consequence, she will forever be remembered as the famous 'Meg o' Meldon', or 'Meg of the Moneybags'.

The Mysterious Disappearance of John Margetts

Dr Greenhow looked upon his young assistant, John Margetts, almost as a son. The lad was bright, willing and keen to learn. True, he could be a bit clumsy at times, being tall and gangly with poor co-ordination in his arms and legs; but wasn't that the case with most 16-year-olds? The good doctor remembered being the same himself at that age.

Dr Greenhow practised medicine from his house in Dockwray Square at the posh end of North Shields, where most of the men of substance and social standing lived. His house stood at the top of a steep hill overlooking the mouth of the River Tyne, which in those days, at the beginning of the 19th century, was alive with commercial activity and crammed with sailing ships from all over the world.

The views from his windows were spectacular, with brilliant sunsets upriver towards Newcastle; wonderful sunrises over the sea to the east, where the gaping mouth of the murky Tyne waited to trap the constant stream of ships on its rocky, silted, wreck-strewn bed, and on the opposite bank of the river, the bustling port of South Shields.

Down the steep hill below his windows was the crowded fish quay, from which the smell of rancid fish guts constantly pervaded the air. The extremely unsightly Low Town clustered around the quay and stretched along the riverbank, crammed with poor, squalid dwellings in filthy streets where offal and effluent were thrown freely into the open, stagnant sewers and onto fly-ridden dung heaps. Here, cholera was endemic and the rate of mortality high.

Dr Greenhow was tired. It was 5 o'clock on the cold, sleety morning of 22nd February 1827, and he had just returned home after being summoned to the house of a poorly neighbour, Mrs Gaunt. He had been so busy with the latest outbreak of cholera that he had hardly slept in the last fortnight, and now all he wanted to do was to go to bed. Yawning and squinting through eyes that felt like sandpaper, he made up a bottle of medicine, then paused for a split second to make a decision that came back to haunt him for the rest of his life. He would send John.

'Wake up, lad. Get out o' yer cot and take this to Mrs Gaunt. I'm going to get some shut-eye.' He waited just long enough to see John put a foot out of his bed before he turned away to his own bedroom.

He woke when it was light a few hours later, feeling cold. The freshening wind was blowing into the house, whistling through the back door, which was wide open. Puzzled, the doctor went to John's room and saw that the lad was not there. His coat and trousers were missing, but his boots were still by the bed, dry and unworn.

Hurriedly, he made his way to the Gaunts' house, just 100 yards away in Tyne Street, and Mr Gaunt assured him that, yes, John had delivered the medicine and gone away again, and Mrs Gaunt felt a lot better this morning thanks.

The next possibility was that the lad had gone to see his mother at the other end of North Shields, but when he called on Mrs Margetts she said she had not set eyes on her son for over a week.

At this point, Dr Greenhow became really worried. The first thing to cross his mind was the existence of the much feared press-gangs. North Shields was a popular port for this activity because of its large community of seamen and its reputation for skilled boatmen. Naval vessels were always short of men because of the huge growth in shipping and because pay and conditions were so bad; and so when sufficient crew could not be found to willingly sign up for a trip, they took men by force.

The doctor's patients had to wait as he scoured the quayside, enquiring on board sailing ships with their ropes clanging on the masts in the wind, talking to the multitude of beggars and vagrants, and visiting alehouses to question the prostitutes and the brawling sailors intent on spending their wages on drink; but no one had seen John, and as time went on he realised that he might never see his young assistant again.

Rumours spread around North Shields that John Margetts had run away to sea to see the world and find his fortune, but Dr Greenhow knew this could not be the case. It was just not in John's steady, unadventurous nature to suddenly take off on a whim; besides which, why would he go half-dressed, without his boots and with no money?

The official North Shields police force did not exist at that time, being established three years later in 1830. Crime was rife around the fish quay, and in order to protect their property the local businessmen had recently established the Association for the

Prosecution of Felons, where they paid into a central fund that provided financial reward for information leading to the arrest and conviction of offenders.

Money was offered and eventually a few people came forward. One man reported that on the morning in question he had seen two men leading another, staggering man down towards the quayside, but he just assumed that the man was drunk.

Later, a mason called Mr Potts told how he heard a scuffle in Tyne Street and someone crying out, 'What are you doing with me?'

Then a woman told Dr Greenhow that she had heard a man cry 'Murder!' and she had seen him being dragged towards a flour mill on the quayside. This was a lead that the doctor could follow up. He found out that a man called Joney Aird, who used to run a stall on the quayside and who lived in an attic above the mill, had vanished immediately after John's disappearance. He got a warrant and, with a watchman, broke into the attic. He found the place was completely empty, except for a ripped shirt collar lying in a corner.

A year went by with no clues as to John Margetts' whereabouts. Then a rumour spread around the town that he had sent a letter to his mother from America, saying that he was alive and well and had made his fortune. His mother, extremely upset, denied it.

Then Dr Greenhow read in the papers that a man named William Hare had been arrested in Edinburgh accused of murder. He had teamed up with an Irish tinker, William Burke, to make a very gruesome living. The pair had started out by digging up bodies from graveyards at night and selling them to surgeons, who needed them for scientific research, for the payment of £7 10s each, which was a good sum of money in those days. Then, when the graveyards became better guarded, they had turned to murder to keep up the supply of corpses. Hare's description seemed to fit the appearance of Joney Aird, the missing stallholder.

Burke and Hare stood accused of 16 murders, and they were due to be tried four days after Doctor Greenhow read the newspaper report; but there was another bad outbreak of cholera in North Shields, which meant that the doctor could not leave his patients to attend the trial. He needed to establish that Joney Aird was in fact William Hare so that he could solve the mystery of John's disappearance. Of course, he had never seen Joney Aird. But he knew someone who had.

He hurried to the quayside and into a paint shop that was situated near to the spot where Joney Aird had kept his stall. The elderly owner of the shop, Mr Park, had known the tall, swarthy stallholder well, and he agreed, in return for a payment from the doctor, to travel immediately to Edinburgh to see if Aird and Hare were in fact the same man.

But Mr Park was not to make that identification. It was a particularly bad December in 1828, and the stagecoach, delayed by fierce storms, arrived the day after the trial. Hare had turned King's evidence, condemning Burke to the gallows, and even though he had been the worst of the pair, he had been granted immunity and set free to start a new life under the name of Mr Black.

Burke was hanged on the day after the trial, the day of Mr Park's arrival. The warder in charge of the body took pity on the elderly man who had travelled so far and, in spite of the fact that it was not Burke who needed to be identified, he kindly offered him a piece of the murderer as a souvenir. And so it was that Mr Park returned home with one of Mr Burke's ears, but no definite solution to the mystery of John Margetts' disappearance.

Dr Greenhow was disappointed but he was still convinced that his unfortunate assistant had been murdered by Burke and Hare and his body sold by them for profit. However, he could never prove it. He had to watch as the Margetts family sank into depression, never to recover from the uncertainty of not knowing what had happened to their beloved John.

The rumours continued for years, the most popular being that the Gaunts had murdered John. Then tales circulated that the young man had been practising as a surgeon with the army in Afghanistan and had been captured by rebels. A soldier from Carlisle stepped forward to confirm that he had seen John in India before his capture. However, shortly afterwards he admitted that he had lied in return for a payment of £100 from the Gaunt family.

Consequently, the Gaunts, who had been desperate to stop the rumours, became prime suspects. The police dug up their garden, watched by a simmering crowd; and when they found bones, the mood became ugly and the watchers threatened to lynch the scared couple. It soon became apparent, however, that the bones were those of a dog that had belonged to a former resident, and finally the shamefaced mob left the Gaunts in peace.

The elegant Dockwray Square eventually deteriorated into slums, and was pulled down. It is now a luxury housing estate around a little park, and the fabulous view includes the two piers embracing the mouth of the Tyne from North and South Shields. Gone are the ramshackle slums and the smells, and the bulk of the shipping. There is no risk of seizure by press-gangs or body snatchers – but people still, occasionally, disappear without trace. And, occasionally, they always will.

The Tragic Radcliffes
of
Dilston Hall

It was the 4th October 1715 and James Radcliffe, the young Earl of Derwentwater, was a troubled man. Under cover of darkness, he had wandered through the wooded grounds of his home, Dilston Hall east of Hexham, and now, deep in thought, he sat on a rock and gazed over the moonlit valley where the Devil's Water murmured its way to the Tyne. He reflected how this estate had belonged to the Radcliffes of Cumberland since the early 16th century, when his great grandfather, Sir Edward Radcliffe of Derwentwater, had married a Dilston heiress. Over the years, the family had been repeatedly subjected to fines and penalties for adhering to their Catholic faith.

James was a peaceful man, loved by all for his kindness and generosity; but circumstances were against him. The government, after the death of Queen Anne the previous year, was adamant that only a Protestant king could sit on the throne, and they had named the Hanoverian George as her successor. Aware of the Earl's childhood friendship with his cousin, the Catholic James Stuart, in France, and hearing rumours of rebellion in the North, they had issued a warrant for the arrest of James Radcliffe and his younger brother, Charles. Luckily, the Earl had been warned in time and for the last couple of months he and Charles had been hiding in various houses and caves around Northumberland.

Stealthily that night, he had revisited Dilston Hall, to be reproached by his pregnant wife, the Countess Anna Maria, for continuing to hide when the gentry were in arms for their rightful sovereign; she had even thrown down her fan and offered to take his sword herself.

The young Earl, a devoted family man with a three-year-old son, had a choice. Should he join his noble but ill-prepared friends the day after tomorrow to march against King George and fight to bring James Stuart to the throne, or should he stay safe in hiding?

Although the Earl was committed to the Stuart cause, he felt that the timing of the uprising was wrong and that there could be a huge loss of life.

His weary eyelids drooped for a moment, but they shot open again at the sound of a woman's voice calling his name. Before him stood a shadowy, hooded female figure in a grey cloak. This apparition spoke to the astonished Earl, warning him that he should be riding for his true king. She gave him a crucifix, which she declared 'should render sword or bullet harmless to him'. Then she disappeared.

Trembling, the Earl leaped up and hurried back to the Hall. His mind was now sure of the action he must take.

On the morning of 6th October, he gathered all the men, horses and arms that he could muster, and he said goodbye to his beloved Countess Anna Maria and his little son. His adventurous brother Charles, who was only 22 and four years younger than the Earl, was hugely in favour of the expedition and eager to be going.

As they left, the omens were bad. The Earl's favourite dog howled in distress, and his horse fought so hard not to carry him away that a precious ring he always wore, a gift from his revered grandmother, dropped to the ground and was lost.

The small party of 30 men crossed the River Tyne at Corbridge and met the main band near Greenrigg, where the River Wansbeck rises. Here, the fatal decision was made to make Tom Forster of Bamburgh, a Northumbrian Member of Parliament, general of the forces. Forster was a Tory and bitterly opposed to the new Hanoverian regime, which had established the Whigs firmly in power. Although he knew nothing of soldiering and was not very bright, he was a Protestant. His leadership would therefore, it was argued, attract more followers to the cause than that of the Roman Catholic Earl, however well loved and trusted he might be.

They marched, steadily increasing in number, across the wild, high moorland to Rothbury to collect recruits, and then down to the marshy coastal plain to declare for James III in Warkworth, Alnwick and Morpeth with little resistance. The plan was then to head south to take the royalist Newcastle; but the city had got wind of their plans and had barricaded the wall gates and sent south for reinforcements. So the Jacobite band headed for Hexham, where they would gather more men – on their way from Galloway – and deliberate their next move.

For a few days, Hexham market place was full of Jacobite rebels. The Earl stayed in a farmhouse near Starward Peel, just 11 miles from Dilston. It would be the last time he would see his Tynedale home.

On 22nd October, with pipes playing and drums beating, the increased band marched north again to Kelso to meet up with the Scots and there the foolish decision was made that was to spell disaster for the Jacobites. The Earl and Charles favoured marching north to secure Scotland, but Tom Forster and the Scottish lords elected to march south to Lancashire. Knowing this was the wrong course, the Radcliffes nevertheless had little choice but to accede.

All went in their favour at Penrith, but the Earl must have gazed at the mountains of the Lake District, his family Derwentwater seat, wondering if he would ever see them again.

The decisive battle came in Preston on 13th November. The Jacobites were claiming the town for James III when a large force of King George's men marched up from the south and a ferocious battle ensued. The Earl and his brother fought valiantly, rallying their men and keeping spirits high by words and example, but General Forster was disheartened and surrendered, much to the disgust of his colleagues.

A verse was written at the time:

> 'Lord Derwentwater to Forster said,
> "Thou hast ruined the cause and all betrayed,
> For thou didst vow to stand our friend,
> But hast proved traitor in the end.
> Thou brought us from our own country –
> We left our homes and came with thee;
> But thou are a rogue and a traitor both,
> And hast broke thy honour and thy oath."'

The Earl of Derwentwater was arrested and taken to the Tower, tried for high treason and sentenced to death.

Massive snowstorms swept the country and with great difficulty, the heavily pregnant Countess Anna Maria made the journey to London to be with her husband. She pleaded with the House of Lords and to King George for his life, and the Earl was told that if he renounced his Roman Catholic faith he would be spared; but he refused to do this, and turned to his faith for comfort in his last days. At his execution on 24th February, he was extraordinarily serene and calm, and as the axe fell there was a groan from the huge crowd assembled there that was 'not unlike the hollow noise of the sea at a distance'.

The lamentations were echoed through the valleys of Northumbria, where, on that night, the 'Red Streams of the North' are recorded to have been seen for the first time. A meteor lit the sky with blood-red crimson streaks, which was believed to be a dreadful omen from heaven.

The Earl's remains were conveyed to Dilston in March, accompanied by his grieving widow. Feeling desolate without the Earl, and meeting a certain hostility from the local populace who were so grief-stricken that they, rightly or wrongly, blamed her for sending him to war, she left, never to return. She delivered a healthy baby girl, but tragically died of smallpox seven years later at the age of 30. Her ghost is said to wander through Dilston Hall watching for her lord's return, an old verse recording:

> 'The Countess wails in Dilston Hall
> But Radcliffe is not there.'

Charles, meanwhile, survived a few months of confinement in Newgate Prison after the uprising, miserably aware of his brother's execution. He was also tried and sentenced to death, but he managed to escape and fled to France, where he fell in love. He married a widowed heiress after proposing to her 16 times (the final proposal being accepted after he had climbed down her chimney) and he raised a family; but he was always restless.

Tragically, the Earl's only son, the Honourable John Radcliffe, died in a horse riding accident in France in 1731, at the age of 19. This left Charles, his uncle, heir to the earldom and the estate although unable to claim them.

Various adventures for the Stuart cause brought Charles to England, and he often revisited Dilston in secret, sadly watching the gradual desolation there, with the gardens overgrown and the gates and walls broken down, wishing he was free to live there and restore the estate. As he wandered around under the cover of evening, the local people took him for the ghost of his late brother, so that the woods and the river, as well as the Hall, gained the reputation of being haunted.

On one occasion on a forest path, Charles came face to face with a bailiff sent from London. The man, terrified at encountering the ghost, turned and galloped back, pursued by a delighted Charles. The chase was short as the bailiff struck his head on a branch and landed on the ground. Afterwards, he swore that the ghost of the Earl had thrown his head at him.

Eventually, Charles was captured while assisting Charles Stuart, the Young Pretender, in an unsuccessful attempt for the throne, and in 1746 at the age of 53, he was beheaded at the Tower. His heart was secretly embalmed by his friends and deposited at Dilston near the remains of his brother. The government gave the estates to Greenwich Hospital and the Hall was destined for demolition.

In 1805 a deputation from the Greenwich Hospital Commissioners, out of curiosity, inspected the remains of the Earl of Derwentwater in the chapel at Dilston, and they were amazed to find on opening the coffin that the body and severed head were in a state of complete preservation, with a sweet, serene expression on his youthful face. A square leaden box was found below the Earl's coffin, containing his brother Charles's heart.

Dilston, in its beautiful setting, was a ruin, but the Radcliffes would always be remembered. A stone cross stands by the roadside between Haydon Bridge and Langley, bearing the inscription: 'To the memory of James and Charles, Earls of Derwentwater, Viscounts Langley, beheaded on Tower Hill, 24th February, 1716, and 8th December, 1746, for Loyalty to their lawful sovereign'.

Half-Hanged
MacDonald

The Bigg Market in the centre of Newcastle has long been the party nucleus of this sociable city; by day, a thriving market-place overlooked by friendly public houses; by night, a lively meeting-place where drink flows, the volume of chatter and laughter rises, and, occasionally, tempers flare.

On the night of 23rd March 1752, Mr Pinkney's tavern in the Bigg Market was full to overflowing with the usual clientele, which included local keelmen, sailors and tradesmen. Sitting in the corner having a quiet drink were a group of soldiers from the 42nd Royal Highlanders, kitted out in full Highland dress. They were staying in lodgings above the tavern.

The Scottish soldiers were not at all happy to be south of the border. Only six years previously, Culloden Moor, near Inverness, had been the scene of a most bloody battle in which thousands of their number had been slaughtered by the English. The Young Pretender, Charles Edward Stuart, was defeated by the Duke of Cumberland, marking the end of the Jacobite cause, and 'Butcher' Cumberland had allowed his men to rape and burn at will throughout Scotland. Following this defeat, the Highlanders begrudgingly agreed to serve King George II, but only in Scotland. However, as time passed, they were finding themselves being posted in England as well.

Feelings were still raw on both sides, with the people of Newcastle remembering the recent history of sieges and bloodshed at the hands of the Scots. Understandably, therefore, relationships between the Highlanders and the locals were not good.

So it was that the group of Scotsmen kept themselves to themselves. Until, that was, a latecomer to their party, Ewan MacDonald, a strapping young lad of 19, came downstairs from his lodgings to join them. Heads turned at the entrance of this striking stranger, who stood head and shoulders above everyone there. The women stared and giggled at his kilt, and the men, fuelled with the bravado that comes with an excess of alcohol, poked fun at him, taunting him with increasingly provoking comments.

HALF-HANGED MACDONALD

MacDonald sat quietly for a while, drinking his beer, his fellow Highlanders telling him to ignore these 'English clowns'. But then his temper snapped and he stood up, grabbed the nearest tormentor, who happened to be a local cooper called Parker, and the two exchanged punches, scattering chairs, tables and glasses in the tussle.

Parker wriggled out of MacDonald's grasp and fled out of the door, but his younger brother Robert was not so fortunate and he was wrestled to the ground by the Scotsman in the doorway. A crowd of people joined in to try to pull the huge man off the smaller man but, when they succeeded, Robert Parker staggered out of the affray with a knife in his neck, and fell to the ground, dead, in a pool of blood.

MacDonald, like a raging bull, stormed back into the tavern, lashing out at anyone he could lay his hands on. He threw one man over a chair, breaking the man's arm, and the remainder of the company tried to escape while the landlord ran for help to the guardhouse around the corner. A party of soldiers arrived and, with difficulty, dragged MacDonald away to lock him up in the nearby Newgate Prison.

The next day at his trial, the repentant soldier apologised for his behaviour of the previous night, claiming that he had stabbed Robert Parker by accident; but he was found guilty of murder and sentenced to hang.

The locals, on the whole decent people with warm, generous hearts under their rough exterior, felt a great deal of sympathy for this young Scotsman who had been goaded beyond tolerance.

On the day of execution, a silent crowd gathered on the Town Moor to see the hanging; but MacDonald had no intention of going silently. He fought all the way. Newspapers reported that he screamed abuse at the chaplain and almost threw the executioner off the scaffold. Struggling to the end, he eventually dropped from the gallows and his body was taken away to the Barber-Surgeons' Hall at Manors for dissection. But the rope had failed to kill MacDonald!

The senior surgeon at the Hall, Samuel Hallowell, a highly respected and talented man, was planning to use the newly hanged Highlander to give a dissection demonstration to his apprentice.

MacDonald's huge body was placed on a mortuary slab and covered by a sheet ready for proceedings. But just as Hallowell was about to remove the covering, he was called away on an urgent case. He told his apprentice, whose look of keen disappointment he had noted, to carry on with the dissection in his absence and to do what he could until he returned, then he rushed away to his emergency.

In the absence of Hallowell's critical eye, the apprentice surgeon was greatly looking forward to the dissection. He uncovered MacDonald's body, picked up a knife, and then gasped when the 'corpse' suddenly opened its eyes and attempted to raise itself up on one elbow.

The terrified student reached out to grab a wooden mallet and smashed MacDonald over the head with it, but the blow was not enough to kill him. The Highlander, summoning his strength, fought back. Again and again the student rained blows on his head until, at last, MacDonald was dead.

Covered in perspiration and gore and breathing heavily from his exertions, the young apprentice sat down to contemplate what he had done. He eventually came to the philosophical conclusion that all was as it should be. Calmly now, he cleaned up and, when his teacher Samuel Hallowell returned from the emergency, it was to find his diligent student engrossed in dissecting the corpse.

Far from feeling remorse about his actions, the student boasted of the incident to his colleagues. News of what had happened soon leaked out and quickly spread around Newcastle. People crowded up to the Barber-Surgeons' Hall wanting to see the dead body. Then, rumours circulated that the Highlander had come back to haunt the building, and the locals stayed away in fear.

A bizarre coincidence occurred a few weeks later when the young apprentice surgeon himself met a grizzly death. He was found in his horse's stable with terrible head wounds. Investigators concluded that the animal had kicked him to death, but the locals believed that the ghost of the Highlander had returned to wreak its revenge. A more credible explanation might be that the revenge was wrought by Ewan MacDonald's Scottish soldier colleagues.

The mallet that killed MacDonald was put on display at the Barber-Surgeons' Hall, where it remained for many years. And the people of Newcastle long recalled the gruesome tale of the dreadful demise of that unfortunate Highlander, half-hanged MacDonald, who fought death to the very end.

The
Hexham Riot

Hexham today is an attractive, picturesque town, its thriving market place flanked on the west side by the benevolent Abbey and on the east side by the ancient Moot Hall. Situated overlooking the beautiful, peaceful Tyne Valley, it is one of the safest places to live in Britain. But Hexham has seen more than its fair share of violence and bloodshed over the years.

Monday, 9th March 1761 was the town's blackest day. Five thousand men, women and children from Northumberland crowded into Hexham market place, and at 2 o'clock on that afternoon, 51 people were killed and up to 300 injured in a tragically violent civil disturbance. Many lives were shattered, but no memorial was erected in Hexham. The event, unique in English history, was barely recorded, and consequently omitted from almost every history book. It was almost as if the authorities wanted to forget that this terrible day had ever happened.

At this time a new and very unpopular law was being enforced around the country. England needed more fighting men. War with the French had stretched the army to its limits, and fears of a French invasion had led to the Militia Act of 1757. This meant a major change in the system of recruitment for the militia, a body of non-professional soldiers whose function was to support law and order at home and to back up the army when required in time of war.

In previous years, the militia was manned by volunteers, but highly inadequate pay and conditions meant that the system had fallen into decay. The new law decreed that numbers for the rank and file would in future be boosted by 'balloting' workers in industry and on the land. Northumberland had to produce 560 able-bodied men between the ages of 18 and 50 for enforced recruitment into the militia, by drawing names in a lottery. Lists of eligible men were affixed to church doors in each area, and meetings were arranged for balloting to be carried out by the local justices and magistrates. The date for Hexham was Monday, 9th March 1761.

One family which would be torn apart on that day was that of William Carter. He had a thriving wheelwright business on the main

35

road through the centre of Hexham. The local roads were so bad that carriages and carts were constantly coming to grief, so his yard was always full of wheels waiting for repair, and William was kept well informed of all the news and gossip from miles around while the drivers, freshly topped up with ale, waited to resume their journeys.

While not afraid to fight for his country, William was very worried that, as an eligible man, he could be forced to serve in the militia for the required three years. Should this happen, he would be unable to provide for his family. His 17-year-old son Samuel, who in a year's time would himself be eligible for the militia ballot, was not yet experienced enough to run the business. William had three other children, his wife Sarah was six months' pregnant with their fifth child, and his elderly mother was also dependent on him. Without his support they would have to seek poor relief or enter the filthy parish workhouse, and he would die before he let that happen.

On the days leading up to 9th March, William heard stories of disturbances at ballot meetings all over the country as working people objected to the selection process, and he was heartened to hear that some had been successful.

At that time, the belief of the property owning classes and the clergy was that manual workers should know their place and do as they were told, so mob protest was the only means the working men had at their disposal to express their opinion.

In Gateshead on 28th February, a crowd of one thousand had delivered a petition to the justices, stating that 'none of us will submit to be balloted after this manner', and expressing a wish that 'men of estates' should hire men for the militia, as formerly. Faced with this potentially explosive situation, the officials backed down and abandoned the meeting.

The people of Northumberland, whose meetings were scheduled for March, were encouraged by this success.

Monday, 2nd March was ballot day for Morpeth. A large crowd of miners, agricultural workers and servants, armed with knives, staves and clubs, gathered outside Morpeth's Sessions Hall for the 10 o'clock start. The justices at first refused to back down but as the mob became uglier and threatened to break down the doors, they took fright and ran away. The victorious crowds then tore up the lists and tickets and burnt them.

Over the next three days throngs marched to Coquetdale, Etal and Belford and at each place the crowd triumphed as before.

The county officials at Hexham, having followed these proceedings with dismay, had plenty of time to prepare for the anticipated trouble. They summoned two battalions of the North York Militia, who at the time were conveniently stationed at Newcastle. So it was that early on the morning of Sunday, 8th March, two companies of each battalion, in total 240 men, marched to Hexham.

Monday, March 9th dawned cold but dry. William Carter and his son Samuel were determined to demonstrate their objections to the balloting at the meeting despite the presence of the militia, which was in any case known to be inefficient and ineffectual. They readied themselves to walk down to the market place in plenty of time before the start of the meeting at 10 o'clock.

Sarah was very subdued. 'Don't go, Will, there's goin' to be trouble,' she pleaded, looking at both him and Samuel. 'If you're not going to think about yerselves, think of me an' the bairns.'

'I am thinkin' of you, that's why I must go and do all I can to stop this ballot goin' ahead.'

'Well then, I'm not stayin' at home worryin'. I'm comin' with ye. Yer mother can look after the bairns today.'

Her face was set. Nothing William could say would change her mind.

As he walked through the yard followed by his largely pregnant wife and his son, he hesitated, glanced at a hefty wheel spoke, which he had planned to take, and then changed his mind. With Sarah by his side, he would be steering clear of trouble.

Groups of people with determined faces were walking in the same direction along the narrow, rubbish-strewn streets. Foul air wafted over them from the tannery at the west end of town, where dog excrement and urine were used to cure the hides; but Hexham's two thousand inhabitants were used to that. Hexham in 1761 was a grim, dank and unsanitary place.

The first thing William and his family saw when they reached the market place was a wall of militiamen surrounding the Moot Hall, a medieval fortified gatehouse constructed from massive blocks of local stone, in which the meeting was about to take place. On the opposite side of the square, where the Abbey towered over a jumble of poor dwellings, people were streaming in from Market Street, paying no attention to a man who was striding around ringing a bell and shouting at the top of his voice for people to return home and stay indoors.

Several protesters strode up to the officers of the militia to present petitions, and they were escorted in pairs through the ranks into the Moot Hall to see the justices who were assembled there. After a short while, the petitioners re-emerged, and when they related to the now considerable crowd that the justices were going to carry on with the balloting, the market place rang with shouts and jeers and the amateur soldiers facing the angry mob started to look increasingly nervous.

At 12 noon people were still crowding into the market place, not only from Hexham but also from over 20 surrounding villages and townships. William clung on to Sarah and Samuel, pulling them back from the front line of soldiers who fixed their muskets with bayonets that they pointed directly into the chests of the protesters. The militiamen were really frightened now as clubs and sticks were waved over their heads and insults were shouted in their faces. Some in the crowd threatened to murder the magistrates, while some tried to bribe the soldiers to lay down their arms.

At 1 o'clock, the magistrates arranged for the Riot Act to be read, commanding the crowd to disperse, the consequences being that if they were still assembled in one hour, they would be arrested and could face the death penalty. This just enraged the protesters further.

A stalemate had been reached that could not go on indefinitely. The frustrated crowd behind started to surge forward and throw missiles. The soldiers advanced and the protesters in front fell back, crushing those in the middle.

Sarah, panic-stricken, was screaming to William that she could not breathe. Unable to take her back through the tightening mass of people, he slowly edged her sideways and forwards. He had previously lost sight of Samuel, but he now spotted the lad standing near the left flank of soldiers where a young officer was remonstrating with some furious protesters. A skirmish ensued as the men tried to seize the bayonets and wrench them from the muskets. Some succeeded in tearing the guns themselves from the soldiers' grasp.

A shot rang out. William saw a soldier sink to the ground, shot with his own musket. Momentarily the noise abated, then more shots were fired from the crowd and the young officer who had been shouting collapsed. Now that the lines of the militia were breached, the protesters forced their way through towards the Moot Hall and the magistrates.

William heard the order to fire on the crowd. He saw as if in slow motion the guns levelled, and then came the ear-splitting noise of gunfire and screaming. Suddenly he was trying to keep his feet as he was carried along by a mass of stampeding humanity. He tried to turn back towards Sarah but it was impossible. His eyes were stinging with the acrid smoke; then he tripped over a body on the ground and he was down on the hard cobbles. Feet kicked him as they fled past, momentarily knocking him unconscious, and he automatically curled into a ball to protect himself.

The firing seemed to go on and on for an eternity, although it was in fact for one full minute. At last the gunfire abated but the screams went on, pitiful screams from injured people, and William recognised one of those voices as that of his son. He raised his bleeding head to see Samuel lying on the ground a short distance away, his leg twisted to the side in an impossible position. All around him was a tragic sight. Bodies of the dead and wounded lay scattered around and soldiers, openly weeping, were beginning to collect weapons from the blood-soaked ground.

William got to his feet and staggered over to Samuel. His stomach lurched as he saw that the lad had a terrible wound to his thigh, with a bone sticking hideously out. He frantically looked around for Sarah. She was lying in front of the Moot Hall, with an oddly serene expression on her face, and a musket ball through her stomach.

Sarah was one of two pregnant women to die that day, along with 47 other protesters and two soldiers. It was impossible to accurately count the wounded as many were able to get away from the scene.

After the event the townsfolk fearfully trickled back to the market place to collect their dead and the badly injured, and the following day torrential rain washed away the blood from the market cobbles.

Samuel survived after receiving good medical attention from the local surgeons, but he was terribly lame for the rest of his life. He became a maker of spinning wheels and a leading figure in the town, and he lived to the ripe old age of 86. William, although he would never forget the horror of that day, managed to carry on for the sake of the remainder of his family, and the Carter business went on to prosper for a further century.

Many people must have lived in fear of imminent arrest for several weeks after the riot. Informers came forward in return for payment from the authorities and, by June, 18 suspected rioters were held in Morpeth jail to await the Newcastle assizes. Most were fined or given short prison sentences. One man was hung, drawn and quartered on 5th October 1761 to serve as an example to those contemplating further acts of high treason; this was Peter Patterson, a 73-year-old farmer from Morpeth, who had been involved in the Morpeth uprising. He had not been at Hexham on that fateful day.

The rioters' protests had been in vain. Subsequent ballot meetings at Hexham, Morpeth and Belford were completed peacefully. However, by the end of the winter in 1762, only a year later, Europe was at peace and the militia was disbanded, no longer required.

The Thorngrafton Find

On a hot day in August 1837, Thomas Pattison was to take into his possession a treasure that would sour his mind and blight the rest of his life – a treasure that would also baffle historians and create an intriguing mystery.

A gang of labourers, glistening with sweat and covered with grime, were that day hewing sandstone from Barcombe Quarry, near the village of Thorngrafton, to provide stone sleepers for the new Newcastle to Carlisle railway. To the west lay the ruins of the Roman Vindolanda Fort, and immediately to the north ran Hadrian's Wall. Both of these structures were built at least in part from Barcombe Hill sandstone almost two thousand years previously, and since then, the ancient quarries dotted around the hill had lain almost untouched in this sparsely populated wilderness, being covered up over time by heather and bracken.

Thomas Pattison's pickaxe clinked onto stone chippings under a mat of heather roots. Pulling all the undergrowth away, he revealed a cleft in the solid rock. There was something hidden inside.

'Hey, lads – look at this,' he shouted as he pulled out a small boat-shaped bronze vessel with a lid and a circular handle big enough to hang around his arm. The workmen crowded around. They undid a little clasp, lifted the lid and found tightly packed inside 63 Roman coins, three of which were gold and wrapped in individual pieces of green leather, and the rest silver.

The men, accustomed to sharing everything, suggested dividing the coins between them. Pattison disagreed. 'We'll likely get more money if we keep 'em aal together,' he argued. 'Look, aa'll gan into Hexham an' see what they're worth, then aa'll split what I get between us.'

Having persuaded the men that this was the best course of action, Pattison spent many of the following nights in the public houses of Hexham showing off the 'button-tops', as he called them. Then, a solicitor and a doctor happened to see the coins and immediately offered him a sovereign and five shillings respectively for them. The quarryman's eyes gleamed. He refused to part with them, realising that he might have in his possession something of greater value than he had at first thought.

Pattison bought his workmates a few drinks and told them he had found out that the coins were almost worthless. They reluctantly accepted his story, and several weeks later the gang moved out of the area to work a different quarry; but Pattison did not go with them. He gave up working as a quarryman and instead supported himself and his sister, with whom he lived in a little house in Thorngrafton, by doing odd labouring jobs and by charging people who wanted to see the curiosity.

A local historian with an interest in Roman coins, a Mr Fairless, was excited when he heard about the discovery. He eventually ran Pattison to ground in the White Hart Inn at Hexham, but was disappointed to discover that the man had become jealously possessive of his treasure and was now unwilling to show it to anyone. The historian suggested that they both go to a private room where the door could be locked and the coins could be examined safely. Pattison eventually agreed, but only after much persuasion and several large brandies.

A few weeks later, news of the find reached the ears of the agents of the Duke of Northumberland, who was lord of the barony of Wark in which the town of Thorngrafton was situated, and who consequently, by the law of treasure-trove, was the rightful owner of the coins. The agents immediately contacted Pattison and asked him to hand over his find. Pattison refused. He hid his treasure, and lay low.

Eventually, Pattison realised he would have to face the problem of the Duke's claims, but he decided that if anyone was going to place the treasure in the Duke's hands, it would be done by himself personally. His mind made up, he set out to trudge the 50 miles to Alnwick, only to find that Hugh, the 3rd Duke of Northumberland, was ill and unable to see him. The Duke's officials offered to deal with the business, but the disgruntled quarryman declined and returned home, now resolving never to give up his treasure to anyone.

Shortly afterwards, the Duke's law agents brought an action against Pattison in order to show the inhabitants of the district that the Duke's rights must be upheld, especially as the excavations for the Newcastle to Carlisle railway could possibly uncover many other valuable Roman discoveries. The case of 'The Duke of Northumberland vs Thomas Pattison' was executed at the Anchor Inn at Haydon Bridge.

THE THORNGRAFTON FIND

Mr Fairless stated at the hearing, 'The defendant showed me the coins. I made a model of the vessel in which they were found, and a catalogue of the coins. There were three gold coins – one of Nero, one of Claudius, and another of Vespasian. There were 60 silver coins; one of Nero, three of Galba, one of Otho, 15 of Vespasian, seven of Domitian, four of Nerva, 15 of Trajan, three of Hadrian, and eleven which I could not appropriate. They were in good condition.' He went on to value the collection at £18.

The jury returned a verdict of £18 damages. Pattison, who had not been represented at the trial, resolved neither to give up the coins nor to pay the £18. Instead, he decided to make himself scarce.

He entrusted the keeping of the coins to his dependable brother, William Pattison, who lived on a little farm at Blenkinsopp, near the Tippalt Burn. Then he disappeared from the district, fleeing to Denbighshire, where a relation of his was gamekeeper to Sir Watkin Williams Wynn of Wynnstay.

For a while he took refuge there and eventually found work at the slate quarries; but then he was tracked down, arrested and locked up in Denbigh gaol as a debtor.

After Thomas Pattison had languished in gaol for some time, his relation the gamekeeper asked Sir Watkin to intervene. Lord Wynn happened to be the brother-in-law of the Duke of Northumberland, and the next time the two met at their London club, they discussed the matter. The Duke exclaimed that he knew nothing at all about it. Always a kindly man, he immediately arranged for Pattison to be offered his freedom.

However, the prisoner declined! He was aware of a statute which stated that no debtor imprisoned for a sum not exceeding £20 should be held in prison for longer than 12 months, and he considered that if he 'stayed put' a little longer until that time was up, the Duke would lose all claims on him and he could keep his treasure without penalty.

The Duke's law officers could make no case for opposition, and Thomas Pattison, after 12 months, was discharged.

He returned to Northumberland to live on his brother William's farm at Blenkinsopp, where he was reunited with his treasure: but he could not settle. He never again did a day's work. His mind wandered in and out of depression, his health failed, and soon he died. He had completely forgotten his promise to his fellow labourers that the proceeds from the find would be shared between them. The coins were now the possession of brother William, who held them with an obsession that almost, but not quite, matched his unfortunate brother's.

Many interested people called at the farm to view the purse and its coins, and all were turned away. Then, in the autumn of 1858, 21 years after the discovery by the quarrymen, Mr Fairless, acting on behalf of his friend Mr Clayton of Chesters, succeeded in persuading the surly farmer to sell the Thorngrafton Find for the sum of 50 shiny, new gold sovereigns.

Mr Clayton, who owned long tracts of the Roman wall together with several forts, was an expert in the study of Roman antiquities, and he was delighted to have possession of the coins to add to his collection. But now it occurred to him that the Duke of Northumberland might still have a lawful right to them. Hugh, the 3rd Duke, had since died, and Algernon the 4th Duke now had the title. Mr Clayton wrote to him about his purchase then waited with baited breath for an answer. To his great relief, the Duke stated how delighted he was that the Thorngrafton Find was now in the most worthy of hands, and that the items were to be added to the treasures in the museum at Chesters Fort.

Now, as the coins were properly examined, a mystery surfaced.

Although most historians believed that Hadrian had built the Roman wall together with the earthen rampart to the south of it about the year AD 120, a few others held to a theory that the two had been constructed separately, with Emperor Severus building the wall around AD 208. However, the 'newest' coins in the vessel appeared to be those from Hadrian's era, the others being suitably aged, indicating that the stones must have been taken from the quarry during his reign. If, on the other hand, Severus had built the wall almost a century later, some coins of subsequent emperors would almost certainly have been present. So far, so good for the Hadrian camp.

But – there was a cuckoo in the nest! A small, ugly, badly corroded coin that no one could previously identify was minutely examined and, to the astonishment of the antiquarians, was shown to belong to the year AD 217, a date after the reign of Severus.

Advocates of Hadrian could not believe it. There must have been a mistake.

The mystery was solved when Mr Fairless heard of the confusion. Shamefacedly, he admitted that when he had first seen the coins, at the White Hart Inn at Hexham, he was afraid that Thomas Pattison would eventually disperse them. Keen to have one for himself, he persuaded Thomas to swap one of the most interesting silver coins for a less interesting one of a later date from his own collection, together with half a crown. Soon after he had made this transaction, there came the inquiry at Haydon Bridge, followed by the hunt for Pattison and the man's imprisonment, and Mr Fairless worried that if it became known that he had swapped one of the coins, he would get into trouble. So he had kept quiet. But, as a historian, he could not stand by and see the advocates of Severus gaining wrongful credibility because of his actions.

Mr Fairless sent the silver coin to Chesters with a letter of apology, explaining that the rogue coin had originally come from his own collection. The historians' relief was so great that he was readily forgiven.

The Thorngrafton Find, coveted by all who had come into contact with it, remained in safekeeping. The original bronze purse and replicas of the coins can now be seen at Chesters Fort Museum on the Roman wall, while the original coins are kept at the British Museum. Against all odds, the entire find has survived intact, thanks in no small part to that unfortunate, obsessive quarryman, Thomas Pattison.

Winter's Gibbet

An eerie sight meets the traveller on the lonely road four miles out of Elsdon at a place called variously Steng Cross or Elsdon Stob. A Saxon cross used to stand here, at the highest point of the ancient drove road down which cattle were driven from Scotland to the English markets. Miles of wild, heather-clad moorland stretch in every direction, backed to the north and west by the wooded Rothbury crags and the far Cheviot peaks, with the view to the south and east sweeping uninterrupted down to distant dots of habitation and the sea. Only the lonely cry of a curlew and the odd bleating of a sheep breaks the silence.

All that remains of the ancient Saxon cross is the stone base, and standing next to that, silhouetted against the wide expanse of sky, is a gibbet with a head hanging from it. The head is facing towards Newcastle, which is just visible as a smudge on the far horizon. It is carved out of wood, the original head having belonged to William Winter, hanged in 1792 for murder.

William Winter had an unfortunate start in life. His family were members of the gypsy Faw Gang, a group of criminals operating from Ryton, on the River Tyne, and his father and brother were both hanged in Morpeth for burglary four years before his own demise on the gallows. He roamed the countryside, often accompanied by other members of the gang, looking for opportunities to steal, and he committed his ultimate crime in the hamlet of Raw, near Elsdon, where an elderly widow named Margaret Crozier lived in a tiny pele tower.

Originally, the tower, called Haws Pele, was one of many such fortified dwellings in Northumberland where cattle could be driven into the ground floor rooms to protect them from the Border Reivers, or mosstroopers, who 'rode the foray', stealing everything they could carry away with them. When peace was restored to the border regions, many of these pele towers became homes, and Margaret Crozier had converted hers into a draper's shop.

Countless travellers passed by this way to avoid paying the turnpikes on the road from Newcastle to Scotland, so Margaret had a good little business with a lot of passing trade, and there were rumours that she had stashed away a tidy sum over the years.

One evening in August 1791, two of Margaret's friends, Bessie Jackson and Mary Temple, both needlewomen, visited her for an hour or two, and left after enjoying a pleasant chat. The next morning a neighbour was passing Margaret's shop and she noticed several reels of thread lying on the ground outside the door. Worried that something was wrong but afraid to investigate herself, she told William Dodds, the local joiner who lived nearby, and he went with her into the house.

A terrible sight met their eyes. Margaret was lying on her blood-soaked bed, her throat slit and her hands and fingers cut to the bone, as if she had been trying to grab an attacking knife. The house had been ransacked, with the dead woman's belongings strewn everywhere.

Neighbours soon gathered outside Haws Pele. They noticed unusual footprints in the soft ground, of boots with a distinctive pattern of nails in the soles. Then later, when Margaret's body was being removed, a knife with a band of iron between handle and blade to strengthen it was found in the bedclothes; but it was discovered that the cut on her neck had not been deep enough to kill her, so she had been strangled with a large handkerchief tied tightly around her neck.

The locals were shocked and infuriated by this savage murder of their old friend and neighbour, and the officers of the parish of Elsdon offered a reward of £5 for information that could help to find the killer – or killers. This was eventually claimed by a particularly observant 11-year-old shepherd boy, Robert Hindmarsh, who had seen three people, a man and two women, acting suspiciously the day before Margaret's murder. His evidence proved to be invaluable; but he did not live long to enjoy his reward. Several years later the unfortunate youth was hunted down by the Faw Gang and was himself murdered.

Robert remembered seeing the trio sitting with their backs against a sheepfold on Whiskershield Common, which overlooked Margaret's house, and the man was dividing food with a banded knife similar to the one found at the murder scene; the boy had also noticed that the man was wearing boots with the same pattern of nails in the soles as was observed outside Haws Pele. He described the man as being powerfully built with long black hair tied back, and the two women as stout and wearing grey cloaks and black bonnets. They also had a donkey with them.

Local constable John Brown was given a description of the suspects and he and two others rode from village to village making enquiries, following the trail of sightings. Several days later, they spotted the man leading a heavily laden donkey down Harlow Hill towards Horsley to the west of Newcastle. It took all three men to subdue and arrest a very belligerent William Winter, who, it was noted, was wearing a suspiciously bloodstained shirt.

Meanwhile, the two women accomplices, sisters Eleanor and Jane Clark, had returned to their encampment on the banks of the Tyne. But it was not long before they were tracked down with the help of local villagers and arrested, after a search of their caravans revealed that they had in their possession a nightcap and apron that Bessie Jackson had made and given to Margaret Crozier.

It transpired that the Clark sisters had visited Elsdon previously on their travels. Margaret had showed them kindness and bought some pieces of crockery from them, and the sisters, convinced that the prosperous-looking shopkeeper was rich, had plotted the robbery with their cousin William Winter.

The three were committed to Morpeth gaol on 3rd September 1791 and their trial was not until the following August at Moot Hall in Newcastle. Winter insisted that he had not killed Margaret, but that on leaving her house he had suspected that she might try to scream for help, so he had sent the sisters back into the house to tie her up. The sobbing women denied any knowledge of the crime, but they were all found guilty and sentenced to be executed.

On the morning of 10th August 1792, the trio were hanged in front of a crowd at Westgate, a horrible death in those days as the victims were made to stand on a cart, and when the cart moved away they hung until they were slowly strangled. Winter, who finally admitted his guilt, cursed and shouted his defiance to his executioners until the end.

The bodies of the two women, who had constantly protested their innocence, were sent off for dissection by surgeons for research purposes, a common practice in those days. Winter's heavy body, followed by a group of onlookers, was transported by long cart from Newcastle to Steng Cross, a journey that would have taken an entire day on the rutted roads. Then it was hung in chains from the gibbet, in sight of the terrible crime, and left there to rot away. The stench from the decaying flesh assailed the nostrils of all who passed, and the skullish grin made them recoil in horror.

Eventually, the bones dropped to the ground, and were buried by local shepherds. When the remains of the body had all gone, a wooden figure was hung in its stead, and when that eventually disappeared, it was replaced by a wooden head.

The events of over 200 years ago will not be forgotten as long as Winter's Gibbet stands for all to see on the wild moors above Elsdon – a chilling reminder of a brutal murder.

Disaster at
New Hartley

New Hartley, situated a mile inland from the sand-dunes and tiny harbour of Seaton Sluice, is an unremarkable Northumberland village with neat estate houses and older modernised pit cottages, a Working Men's Club and a few shops, set amidst pleasant country-side. But if you scratch the surface of the surrounding green hills, you will find man-made slagheaps lying underneath. Until half a century ago this land was a grey lunar landscape of spoil tips and pit-heaps. For tens of generations coal mining was the only work that many in the area knew, and in 1862 Hartley Colliery was the scene of a terrible disaster that changed coal mining in England for ever.

In the early 1800s coal was king, deemed more important than gold and silver to the economy. Coal not only provided heat, it fuelled the Industrial Revolution, which turned Britain into the factory of the world. Deprived of its coal, Britain would have faced financial ruin, with no forges and foundries to produce steel for the manufacture of everything from railways and ships to cutlery. More than 15,000 pitmen were employed in South East Northumberland, heroes descending into the 'Bowels of Hell' for little reward, always with the shadow of death or serious injury literally hanging over their heads. Their working hours were long and education almost non-existent, ensuring that they had no opportunities to escape a system that was akin to serfdom.

Unrest at the terrible working conditions came to a head in the great strike of 1831. Miners visited collieries, damaging machinery and making sure the blacklegs had no chance to keep the pits working. The men were victorious, one of the results being the establishment of a 12 hour working day for boys (some as young as six) instead of one of up to 18 hours; but the concessions were small and the hardship continued.

Hartley Colliery was operated by Messrs Carr Bros on land owned by Lord Hastings, who spent most of his time on his estates in Norfolk, rarely venturing up to the coalfields of Northumberland. The miners of Hartley, like miners everywhere at the time, were paid a pittance by the mine owners, and were forced to live in tiny, dilapidated cottages, often with large families sharing only two rooms. Most of the men worked in the mine, and the women struggled endlessly against dirt and squalor. But the community spirit was strong. People grew up together, worked together, and married into each other's families. They shared everything, including their fears – and their worst fears were eventually realised.

At 10 am on 16th January 1862, a Thursday morning, Tom Watson had just finished his shift below ground. His job as a 'hewer', cutting the coal from the coalface, was dirty and exhausting, but although he was anxious to get home he stopped to have a 'bit banter' with his mate who was relieving him. Then, as he had done countless times before, he walked to the pit shaft and stepped into the open-sided cage with seven other men to ride to the surface. One of the men, William Sharpe, was an old friend of Tom's, and they had just greeted each other when there was a sudden ear-splitting crack, and a tremendous crash of stones and timber fell about the cage. The cast-iron beam of the pumping engine, which weighed 43 tons and projected from the engine-house right over the mouth of the pit, had snapped in two, and half of it had fallen down the timbered pit shaft.

There was only one shaft at Hartley Colliery, and now it was blocked solid with a mass of woodwork, iron and stone. All the miners below were trapped. The accident had happened at the most unfortunate time possible, the changeover, with men from both the fore-shift and the back-shift caught underground.

The corner chains holding the cage had snapped, and Tom found himself hanging on for dear life to its slanting base. All was complete darkness, with thick dust choking his lungs. He heard cries from below, then William Sharpe cried out in pain by his side. Tom shouted, 'How many's hangin' on?' Another voice, that of Ralph Robinson, shouted back at him. So there were three of them. The other five occupants had been thrown down the shaft.

'Old Sharpe' had a very bad injury to his leg. He managed to produce a match and strike it, but copious amounts of water dropping down the shaft because of the destruction of the pump soon extinguished the feeble light. He was distressed as one of the voices crying out from below was that of his 16-year-old son George, who had been tipped from the cage down onto the wreckage. Tom felt around and located the 'tapping' wire, which was used for stopping and starting the cage, hanging down the shaft, and he said he would try to reach him.

Carefully he descended, aware that he could fall at any moment into the abyss below. Thoughts of his four children flashed into his mind. Their mother had died giving birth just five months ago, and if he died they would be orphans. He must survive for them!

With great relief he reached the bottom, but he was greeted with the moans of dying men half buried in the wreckage. Young George Sharpe was breathing his last, and Tom comforted him and the others as best he could, but after several gruelling hours, he was on his own, surrounded by the broken bodies of his friends.

It was now about 5 pm and as yet there was no sign of rescue. Shivering with the cold, and in total darkness, Tom knew he had to try to climb back up the shaft. He gripped the wire that he still held in his hand, but his strength had gone and he swallowed down a feeling of hopelessness. Then, gazing up into the blackness, he saw a light, which has never been explained, shining in the shaft and showing him a ledge where he could rest out of the way of the falling water and debris. Another six long hours passed, but Tom was sure rescue would come. Then he heard hammering from above, and voices shouting. A rope was lowered with a lantern attached. William Sharpe, who had been hanging on to the cage all this time, was first to go up, but he was so weak that he fell from the rope and crashed to the ground not far from Tom. He died instantly.

Next to go up was Ralph Robinson, who ascended with no problems; and then it was Tom's turn. He was weak, soaking wet and numb with cold. As he was pulled to the surface, past broken timbers and cascading water, there was a roar and the side of the shaft caved in beneath him; but he made it in one piece. He surfaced at midnight, 14 hours after the start of the disaster.

By Friday evening, a large portion of the debris had been cleared from the shaft by brave volunteers from surrounding collieries keen to help their fellow miners. Hopes were high that the men trapped below would soon be home with their families. All through Friday night the dangerous work continued and the prisoners were heard 'jowling', communicating the fact that they were still alive by knocking and making as much noise as possible. But by Saturday morning, the jowling had stopped.

A deep and solemn silence prevailed over the village of New Hartley. No children played and cold agony marked the faces of the women hoping against hope that their men would come home.

At the pithead, the twisted heap of metal that was the cage lay beside the tall engine-house. Two huge fires for heat and light burned constantly near the shaft, where relays of men were lowered one by one down the gaping black pit by means of a heavy chain. The debris was loaded into a basket and carefully passed upwards, an agonisingly slow and perilous process. Groups of people clustered in anxious groups through the bitter cold and snow of Saturday night, and again through Sunday, which brought crowds of sightseers to gawp at the scene.

The weary watchers continued to be disappointed, becoming impatient with the slow progress, until 4 am on Tuesday morning when a signal of distress was received from below, and a rescue worker was quickly brought up after a great rock fall, which had almost cleared the shaft. Optimism turned to despair when more of the rescuers were brought up, some staggering between comrades and some carried off unconscious, suffering from the effects of the deadly gas carbon dioxide, which had been released in a rush as the shaft had been unplugged. Later that morning a cat was sent down the pit, and after some time it was brought up hardly able to stand. One of the chief rescuers stated, 'The case is as bad as it can be,' and few then held out any hope that the trapped men would come out alive.

A means of ventilation was rapidly installed to allow work to proceed. Brave volunteers continued to risk their lives in the unsafe pit, which was still full of gas, to find the miners, and it was 5 pm on Wednesday when they came upon the first bodies, lying side by side, with tiny pit boys as young as 10 clinging to their fathers.

The dreadful news flew like lightning through the village. There were terrible scenes at the pithead, where distraught families waited for the bodies to be drawn out. A barrier had to be erected to keep people away from the shaft. It took until the following Sunday for all the corpses to be retrieved.

The mass funeral was held on 26th January, the second Sunday morning after the terrible disaster. The day was bright and beautiful, but at almost every window in New Hartley the curtains were closed. The procession to Earsdon cemetery was four miles long. Only 25 men remained alive in the village, the rest, 204 good Northumbrian men and boys who had toiled in hazardous conditions to make a very small living for themselves and their families, were dead.

Medals were given to the brave men who put their own lives at risk in the rescue. Many acts of extreme heroism were performed by ordinary Northumbrian pitmen bent on rescuing their comrades, selfless acts that were carried out as a matter of course with no thought of reward, just the wish to help in any way they could.

One positive thing to come out of the disaster was legislation leading to the banning of one-shaft mines in this country. Each mine in future needed to have at least two shafts, which would give the men an escape route if one shaft should collapse, and so prevent a similar disaster from ever happening again.

Letters from
the Wall

The Roman fort at Vindolanda, not far from Bardon Mill, is a treasure chest of hidden secrets. Its stone foundations lie exposed on a grassy plateau that overlooks the steep Chineley Burn valley. Wild, sparsely-populated countryside surrounds it in every direction, and a mile to the north the most spectacular mid-section of the Roman wall snakes over lofty crags, commanding an endless view for miles over the moorland and forests of Northumberland towards the far distant Scottish border.

The original fort was constructed in wood around AD 85, almost 40 years before Hadrian decided to build the wall to mark the northern frontier of Britain. The Roman army had subdued the country from south to north, and the role of Vindolanda Fort was to guard the central section of the recently built Stanegate Road, the vital east–west supply route between Carlisle and Corbridge. Timber walls and turrets surrounded an area of three and a half acres on which were built barracks for the men, the Commanding Officer's house, the headquarters building, stables, workshops, granaries and store-houses, a chapel, bath-houses and latrines to sit a dozen men at a time. A civilian settlement was established outside the walls, populated by traders, prostitutes and families wanting to be near the security of the fort. A whole town grew where there had previously been scrubland and bog.

The troops were far from home, made up of men from other parts of the Roman Empire, primarily the Lowlands. They must have been homesick, but there had been little evidence of their maintaining contact with friends and family until, on a spring day in 1973, Robin Birley, principal archaeologist at Vindolanda Fort, made an amazing discovery. While digging he unearthed two small, thin fragments of wood, which, at first sight, appeared to be oily wood shavings, but as he examined them more closely, he noticed, with a jolt of excitement, what appeared to be ink hieroglyphs. He hardly dared to believe his eyes when, after carefully cleaning the pieces and prising them apart with a knife, he saw they were covered in tiny, spidery writing.

The text was in Latin, dated between AD 95 and AD 110. It was a letter sent to a soldier serving at Vindolanda Fort from a friend or relative. The legible part reads:

'I have sent you ... pairs of socks from Sattua [unknown place] two pairs of sandals and two pairs of underpants ... Greet ...Tetricus and all your messmates with whom I pray that you live in the greatest good fortune.'

This proved to be only one of hundreds of written tablets found after painstaking excavation on the same site, all dated within the timescale of the first find and including both official and private correspondence of the men and women who lived at Vindolanda. Over two hundred had been thrown onto a rubbish pile almost two thousand years ago and set alight, but perhaps a heavy cloudburst had put out the fire. Organic matter piled on top of them had created the ideal conditions for their incredible state of preservation.

The majority of the tablets were thin slivers of wood, around two mm thick, cut from the then plentiful local trees of birch and alder. They were smoothed to take writing in ink on one or both sides, then scored down the centre and folded. The pens used were hard reeds sharpened at one end, or metal nibs in wooden holders, and the ink was made from lamp-black and gum mixed with water. Longer letters or lists of goods were written over several tablets, which were joined in a concertina fashion by thongs. Some of the tablets were recessed pieces of pinewood coated with wax, written on with a sharply pointed metal stylus, which sometimes penetrated through the wax, leaving marks on the wood.

Most of the letters concerned the household and affairs of Flavius Cerialis, an officer of high status, outside whose house the letters were dumped. Cerialis lived in the Commanding Officer's house with his wife, Sulpicia Lepidina, their three children and their slaves. Only officers were allowed to marry, and the wives who accompanied their husbands to their postings dwelt in luxury compared to the troops; but it must have been a shock to Lepidina when she first arrived at Vindolanda around AD 95. She would have arrived via the Stanegate Road, exhausted after a long journey with her children and her immediate possessions, sitting on a bumpy carriage pulled by mules. The wooden fort on its plateau would have appeared to her to be little more than a building site, as it was being enlarged to double its original size to accommodate her husband's battalion. It would have been surrounded by mud, busy workmen, marching soldiers, horses and scruffy civilians erecting their humble dwellings outside the walls. A large bath-house was under construction near the fort walls, and, as the footprints of dogs, cats, pigs, sheep, goats and cattle have been found imprinted on some of the bricks, there were obviously plenty of four-legged animals roaming around.

Lepidina would have been relieved to find that her house had its own bath-house and toilet, with underfloor heating and fresh reeds to walk on; but she must have felt the pangs of homesickness in this cold, draughty place far away from anywhere. However, she did make at least one friend. She received a birthday invitation:

'Claudia Severa to her Lepidina greetings. On the third day before the Ides of September [September 11th], sister, for the day of the celebration of my birthday, I give you a warm invitation to make sure that you come to us, to make the day more enjoyable for me by your arrival, if you are present. Give my greetings to your Cerialis. My Aelius and my little son send him their greetings. I shall expect you, sister. Farewell, sister, my dearest soul, as I hope to prosper, and hail. To Sulpicia Lepidina, wife of Cerialis, from Severa.'

It is thought likely that Severa lived seven miles to the west at Carvoran Fort. Her husband, Aelius Brocchus, was also a good friend of Cerialis, which is probably how the two women met. Cerialis obviously enjoyed a bit of hunting, as this letter shows:

'Flavius Cerialis to his Brocchus, greetings. If you love me, brother, I ask that you send me some hunting nets ... you should repair the pieces very strongly.'

There would have been plenty of wild game around to keep him happy, including deer, wild boar and wolves.

Cerialis would have much to keep him occupied, while Lepidina spent her time managing the house and the slaves and bringing up her children. Either she or one of the slaves may have been teaching them how to write, as written in shaky capital letters on the back of a discarded letter is a line from Virgil's *Aeneid*, thought to be a writing exercise. At the end it is marked by the term for 'sloppy work'!

Luckily for Lepidina, times were peaceful and she would not have had to worry overmuch about Cerialis's safety in this posting. However, the troops were still kept busy with a multitude of tasks including training, hunting down deserters, delivering mail, and putting down minor skirmishes. Cerialis received this letter from one of his cavalry troop commanders out stationed somewhere:

> 'Masculus to Cerialis his king, greetings. Please, my lord, give instructions on what you want us to do tomorrow. Are we all to return with the standard, or just half of us? … most unfortunate and be well disposed towards me. My fellow soldiers have no beer. Please order some to be sent.'

This could have been a way of alerting Cerialis to the tardiness of the quartermaster, who was failing in his duty to keep the men supplied with beer. Lepidina would have had no such problems with food and drink. The fort was well supplied with a huge variety of foodstuffs, including apples, honey, nuts and olives and there is a letter about a gift of 50 oysters. Large quantities of meat were consumed, the favourite being pork. Also, copious amounts of wine and beer were shown to have been drunk at dinner parties hosted by Cerialis and Lepidina. On at least one occasion they entertained the Governor of Britain when he was visiting to inspect the northern frontier.

The severe winters would have been the hardest time for everyone. At least Lepidina would not have been plagued with midges at this time of the year; a lady's cap was found made out of moss to fend off the biting insects. But the supply of food and other goods would have been disrupted by snowfalls. One letter, thought to have been from one officer to another, states that the road to Catterick, the major north–south route, was so bad it was unfit for wheeled traffic and could injure the animals. It also complains about the price of cattle hides, and that the recipient owed the sender money:

> '… I have several times written to you that I have bought about five thousand sacks of grain, on account of which I need cash. Unless you send me some denarii, at least five hundred, the result will be that I shall lose what I have paid out of my own pocket as a deposit, about three hundred denarii and I shall be in an embarrassing position.'

Lepidina would have had no worries about money. Cerialis would have been paid handsomely and she would have had the best of everything available, with servants and slaves to shield her from any unpleasantness. One fragment of Cerialis's correspondence refers to deserters, so military life would have been hard and miserable for some. The maintenance of discipline was essential and the records show that centurions were notorious for their use of the swagger sticks on lazy men. This appeal for mercy could have been from either a soldier or a civilian to Cerialis:

'... I implore your mercifulness not to allow me, a man from overseas and an innocent one, about whose good faith you may enquire, to have been bloodied by rods as if I had committed a crime.'

This man was obviously not from the area. One report described the locals as Brittunculi, the 'wretched Britons', and Cerialis and Lepidina would have had little to do with them as they were clearly held in some contempt.

Cerialis and his family finally left Vindolanda in AD 105, sent to join Emperor Trajan's army on the Danube. A letter from Brocchus wishes him well:

'... We pray, brother, that what you are about to do will be most successful. It will be so, since it is both in accord with our wishes to make this prayer on your behalf, and you yourself are most worthy.'

So after ten years, Lepidina was on the move again, perhaps this time to a war zone. She would have said her farewells to Claudia Severa, and with some trepidation gathered her children and her personal slaves and set off once more to be with her husband, never to return to Northumberland. Was she sorry to leave? Her children had grown up here; she doubtless had happy memories and had enjoyed a safe life so it is more than likely that she was sad. The letters she left behind would have been gathered together in a pile with Cerialis's old files, thrown onto the rubbish heap outside, and set alight.

Almost two decades later, the Emperor Hadrian visited Britain and decided to establish the frontier with a continuous wall; then a decade after that, the attempted conquest of Scotland led to years of fighting and the destruction and rebuilding of the forts. Amazingly, after all this activity and all this time, the oldest written material in Britain and the earliest example of handwriting by a woman ever found was discovered, preserved in the ground.

Over 1,500 writing tablets have been uncovered so far, and excavations are continually revealing more. They are priceless and fascinating, like ancient echoes from the past, bringing to life the people who lived so long ago in this beautiful, wild place.

The Hermit
of
Warkworth

Atiny hermitage hewn out of the solid sandstone cliff, half a mile upstream from the majestic Warkworth Castle, has attached to it a tale of love and tragedy, at a time when men were tough and women made them prove it!

The hermitage is in a beautiful spot, overlooking the tranquil River Coquet, overhung and almost hidden by trees, ferns and mosses. Twenty stone steps lead up to the arched doorway through which is a little porch with a stone seat at either side. Inside are three rooms just big enough to walk a dozen paces around; first is a tiny chapel, behind that the sacristy where the hermit could store his sacred vessels, and next to that the hermit's dormitory. The chapel is skilfully carved with columns against the walls and ribs under an arched ceiling. At the end is a stone altar, and to the right under a two-light window lies the figure of a woman, her hands raised in prayer. Kneeling at her feet is the figure of a man, his right hand supporting his head, his left hand pressed to his heart as if in sorrow.

A hermit first lived here in the mid 14th century, and it is said that anyone passing by at that time either in a boat or on the footpath on the opposite bank could hear his wails of anguish and remorseful cries. By day or by night in the flickering candlelight, in summer or in freezing winter, he remained in solitude desperately praying on his knees for forgiveness. But the story goes that the tortured soul had once been an eager young knight attached to Lord Percy of Alnwick and Warkworth, full of life and vigour and determined to prove himself to the woman he loved.

Lord Percy took a great interest in his knights, for he relied on them to protect his huge estates from the marauding Scots. Although he already owned the magnificent Alnwick Castle, he had recently been granted the equally magnificent Warkworth Castle by King Edward III who realised that, after regular attacks, the castle needed a local and powerful presence. On a hill overlooking Warkworth and the River Coquet, the castle dominated the village in every way and the Percys kept a tight hold on their assets by residing here in the winter months, and at Alnwick five miles up the coast in the summer.

It was at the latter that Lord Percy decided to hold a great banquet – and he was famed for these – with minstrels and tumblers and a spectacular show of precious plate bearing every kind of meat imaginable. He had been approached by one of his best knights, Sir Bertram, Lord of Bothal Castle, near Morpeth, who had asked his permission to ask for the hand of the beautiful Isabel, daughter of the neighbouring Lord of Widdrington. The match was agreeable to Lord Percy, so he invited Isabel and her father as honoured guests to the banquet, and watched events with amusement.

Isabel was obviously delighted when Sir Bertram made his official marriage proposal, but as was the custom in those days, she was not so easily won. After some consideration, she sent one of her maids to present him with a shining helmet and the message that she would be his bride once he had proved himself worthy of her by performing some brave deed in a noble enterprise.

Lord Percy, entering into the spirit of things, announced that he had decided to make a raid into Scotland to search out the troublesome clans and prevent further attacks, and the date was set for Bertram to ride away under the Percy banner to demonstrate his worth.

Bertram fought valiantly in a series of bloody battles, proving his bravery again and again. But the Scots were not easily beaten, and he almost lost his life when a Scottish battle-axe crashed through the helmet that Isabel had given him and cracked open his skull. His younger brother and his friends carried him to the nearby Wark Castle on the border, where he lay between life and death for several weeks, asking constantly in his delirium for Isabel to come to him.

A message was sent to Isabel, and when she heard of Bertram's plight she bitterly blamed herself. Full of remorse, she insisted that she go to him immediately to help nurse him back to health. Her father chose two of his most trusted men to accompany her, and the trio headed north for the border.

The weeks passed and Bertram slowly improved, but there was still no sign of Isabel. He walked around the huge fortified walls and along the banks of the Tweed when the coast was clear of the ever-threatening Scots, gradually regaining his strength and going mad with anxiety, wondering why she had not come. As soon as he was able to ride, he set off to Widdrington with his brother, who had stayed with him while he recovered.

When they reached Isabel's home, her father was away and a maid told them that Lady Isabel had left for Wark as soon as she had received the message, and that she should have arrived there long since. Bertram realised with dismay that she must have been waylaid and, weak and ill though he still was, he set off immediately to find her.

He and his brother parted company and searched independently to cover more ground. Often in peasant disguise in order to elicit more information, Bertram scoured the countryside. Eventually, after many frustrating days, he heard that a beautiful lady had been imprisoned by a Scottish chieftain in the Castle of Hethpool, in the Cheviot Hills. Bertram knew that this particular chieftain had been an admirer of Isabel, so he felt hopeful that his search might soon be over.

With his sword hidden under a roughly woven peasant's cloak, Bertram rode to the castle, which was a fortress of exceptional strength made of huge, hard volcanic boulders. The hills rose darkly all around the place, seemingly deserted except for a scattering of sheep. It was dusk and Bertram found a place to rest where he could watch the castle and where he and his tethered horse would be hidden from sight behind a rocky outcrop. Exhausted, he was soon nodding off to sleep.

A sound woke him. A woman's cry. He started up and peered around the rock. The moon briefly illuminated the scene and he saw Isabel lying on the ground below the castle wall, with a man wearing a Highland bonnet and cloak leaning over her. At once consumed with rage and fear for her safety, he grabbed his sword and he charged at the man, shouting 'Vile traitor! Let my lady go!' His sword swung in a mighty arc and cleanly severed the man's head in the hated bonnet from his shoulders. Isabel had leaped up in an attempt to shield the man, but the blade struck her in the breast and she fell, mortally wounded.

Bertram was shocked to the core. He flung himself down to cradle Isabel's head as she whispered her last words.

'That was your brother come to save me. We climbed down a rope ladder – I fell and hurt my ankle.'

For two hours after her last breath, Bertram did not move. Then, like a man in a trance, he loaded the bodies of the two people he loved most in the world onto his horse and started on the long journey home.

Sorrow and remorse remained with Sir Bertram for the rest of his life. After returning to Warkworth, he gave away his possessions to the poor and asked Lord Percy's permission to create the hermitage so that he could retire from the world to spend the rest of his days in penitence.

In the chapel he carved on an altar tomb the image of Lady Isabel, his lost love, and at her feet that of himself, her grief-stricken knight. Above the doorway, just inside the entrance, is the inscription in Latin: 'My tears have been my meat day and night'.

The story of Sir Bertram has been passed down as a legend, and although he did exist, officially no one knows who the first hermit of Warkworth was. At the terrible time of the Black Death in 1348, the Percys would have welcomed prayers from a hermit for their salvation, and they would have supported him. Over the centuries, the original hermit was followed by successors and the hermitage was adapted and extended to provide a more comfortable lifestyle. The Percys continued to prosper, although not without some major disasters, and the little hermitage remains, a fascinating piece of medieval handiwork and a reminder of one of the great tragic stories of the past.

A
Border
Tale

The people immediately north and south of the English/Scottish border come from the same original stock, the families having intermarried for centuries, long before the artificial line was drawn on the map. Many tragedies happened on this beautiful, wild stretch of land, with constant warring between the English and the Scots ripping families apart, often leaving the women demented with grief. One such woman was Barbara Moor.

It all started one day in 1616, at the Whitsome Fair directly north of where the River Till meets the River Tweed. The young Barbara was there with her father and her brother, and she caught the eye of her husband-to-be, Jonathan Moor, a prosperous farmer. He was completely bowled over by this feisty, dark-haired girl, and, not one to waste time, he immediately proposed to her and invited the family to visit his farm, which was several miles to the south-west of Berwick.

Barbara's father was ambitious for his daughter. He looked around Jonathan's property, nodding to himself, before he gave his opinion, 'Aye, I'm happy enough for ye to marry my lass, but ye could dee wi' more cattle on the place.'

This was a challenge to which Jonathan was quite capable of rising. He came from a family of Border Reivers, a tough breed of fighting men who, over the last three centuries, had learned to survive in this lawless corner of England by raiding and cattle rustling.

'Then I'll gan reivin' ower the border 'yon side of Coldstream for Cunningham's herds,' Jonathan promised, already eagerly anticipating the stealing of some fine beasts belonging to his greatest enemy, a man whose family had many times in the past raided his own farm. Barbara's brother Duncan, always looking for adventure, said he would go too.

Little did Jonathan know that this reckless act he was planning was to reverberate through the years in a series of tragic consequences.

Barbara had a terrible premonition. She was aware that she had inherited the 'second sight' from her mother, now dead, and the pictures in front of her eyes of blood and doom stretching far into the future scared her. But the men laughed away her warnings. The next night, Jonathan and Duncan, each with two companions, crossed a ford over the River Tweed and rode onto Cunningham's land.

The gate into the field, which enclosed scores of the finest beasts in the area, was easily broken down; but as soon as the men started to drive the cattle out, a man rose from a stone lookout tower at the other side of the field and began to strike at a bell. The clanging and the bellowing of the now stampeding cattle made an almighty din. Jonathan knew the game was up.

'Ride for yer lives, lads,' he shouted.

As he looked around he saw Duncan draw his pistol and fire at the watcher in the tower, who fell a dead weight to the ground.

'Duncan, ye fool,' he shouted angrily. The sound of horses' hooves galloping towards them drove the raiders wildly towards the river; then Cunningham and his men caught them up and, swords drawn, one of the first to fall was Duncan. The other side was stronger, and of the four companions, one was killed and three surrendered.

Confronted by Cunningham himself, Jonathan fought valiantly until a sword thrust killed his horse and he fell. His opponent also fell and was knocked unconscious. Jonathan dragged himself to a nearby wood and, still clutching his sword, he passed out; but not for long. Terrifying howls of pursuit roused him, and he forced himself awake, to see a great bloodhound emerge from the moonlit night. It leapt onto him, but Jonathan still had enough wits about him to thrust his sword into the hound's chest. He forced himself upright and stumbled to the river, to the ford, and waded over to start the long trek home.

Barbara was waiting for him, and was distraught to find that her prophecy had been correct. Jonathan could not tell her father whether Duncan was dead or alive, but Barbara had no doubt that he was dead. Not long afterwards, the three surviving companions returned home, saying that they had been released when the wounded Duncan had owned up as being the one who had shot Cunningham's brother, the watcher in the tower. Cunningham had then ordered that Duncan should be thrown from the tower to his death in retribution.

Barbara's father died mourning his only son, and Barbara, aware that Jonathan was miserably contrite, and still in love with him despite his foolishness, agreed to marry him. For the next 25 years the couple lived comfortably and had seven sons, the first two and the youngest two twins; and as the boys grew strongly into manhood, Barbara almost forgot her previous horrific premonition.

In August 1642 the Civil War between King Charles I and Parliament broke out in England. Although England and Scotland had one monarch, their individual aspirations were not so united, and the Scots remained uninvolved until, in 1643, fed up with the King's attempted imposition of Roman Catholicism, they agreed to help the Parliamentary side. Berwick, as it had so many times in history, again found itself in the middle of a bloody conflict.

Jonathan cared little about the war until, hearing that Cunningham and his three sons had decided to fight on the side of the King, he resolved to ride out with his sons in support of Cromwell. Barbara's black visions of blood and horror returned, and she was desolate.

'If ye go ye'll ne'er ride home again,' she wailed; but nothing she could say would persuade her sons not to go, and Jonathan would not let them set off without him. The two forces met in battle, and Barbara's husband and seven sons were all killed, as were Cunningham's three sons.

Barbara, mad with grief, left her house and wandered the countryside, sleeping in woods and ditches, turning into a crazy but harmless woman whom people both feared and pitied.

Cunningham had survived the battle and, while still mourning his three sons, his middle-aged wife died giving birth to a fourth son. This little boy became his life, the focus for all his love and tenderness. The baby grew into a fine little lad, and when he was four years old, his father proudly took him to the fair at Whitsome.

The doting father left his precious son for only a few minutes in the care of a servant while he clinched a deal on some cattle, but when he returned, the boy had disappeared. The servant emerged from a nearby inn, admitting that he had thought the youngster would be fine for a minute or two while he had a drink. Desperately they searched, for hours, around the fair and the surrounding countryside. But the boy could not be found.

Poor Cunningham lived on in misery until, to ease his suffering and loneliness, he adopted a nephew to bring up as his heir.

In all, seven years passed, until a violent, stormy night when one of his men informed him that an old woman had taken shelter in the old shed and he feared she would die with cold, saying, 'It's that auld daft wife I've seen runnin' aboot.'

Cunningham took a lantern and went with him to the shed to find a figure, hardly human, ragged and drenched and wild looking. He looked on her with pity. 'Come in and bide by the fire, woman, and get some food an' drink inside ye.'

'Cunningham,' she screeched, 'ye cursed murderer. I'll ne'er set foot in your hoose.' She started to run away, but turned to shout back at him, 'Yer bairn lives. You may see him, but you winna ken him and he winna ken ye.' Then she fled into the stormy night, leaving the ageing man staring after her in bewilderment.

Wandering the border country as she did, with people ignoring her as if she was invisible, nothing much escaped Old Barbara's attention. She had seen Cunningham's son only a short time before, walking down a farm track near Wooler in Northumberland. He was a friendly lad and when she asked him his name, he told her: 'Patrick Reed.'

'That's no' yer name.' She smiled slyly. 'Yer real father lives an' ye were born to riches, but I winna tell ye who he is.'

After she had run off into the woods, Patrick, a happy, carefree boy, soon thought little more of the encounter with the wild and crazy old woman. When he reached home he didn't even think to mention it to the man who he knew had taken him in as a child and whom he looked upon as his father, Sandy Reed.

Sandy was a farmer whose wife, just like Cunningham's, had died giving birth, in this case to a daughter. Seven years previously, he had gone south to Morpeth Fair for a few days to do business. Before riding back to Wooler, he had met up with some friends for a 'bit crack' and a few drinks, and a few drinks more, the result being that when he was almost home he fell asleep and toppled off his horse onto the tufted marsh grass. He eventually woke with the bright moon shining in his eyes and a small child wailing and crying and cold as ice, huddled in the crook of his arm. Astonished, he gathered the little boy, who was wearing only rags, to him and he shouted a few times, but the night was utterly still. There was nothing for it but to take the child home with him. He called him Patrick, after his own father.

Sandy's young daughter, Anne, took to the boy as soon as she saw him. For years the pair were great friends, then as they grew into their teens they fell in love and decided to marry, and the day came when they intended to announce their betrothal at the next Whitsome Fair.

The day of the fair dawned sunny and dry as Sandy, Anne and Patrick set off to ride the few miles over the border. The old farmer was intent on buying some good cattle. There were lots to choose from, but the best he could see belonged to old Cunningham, who had come with his nephew and a few of his men. A bargain was struck, and the two farmers sealed it by drinking each other's health many times over, swapping increasingly boastful stories about the exploits of their youth. Then Sandy made a bet that Patrick could beat Cunningham's nephew in a wrestling match.

The two lads had also been drinking, and they needed very little encouragement to prove their strength in a good-natured fight. Stripping off their jackets, they stood up and, in front of a gathering crowd, each tried to floor the other.

The crowd swelled, and a great cheer went up when Patrick won the fight.

'Try them wi' the sword,' called Cunningham, and the crowd cheered again. Someone gave them swords. The two lads faced each other. Soon blood was dawn, tempers rose, and the contest became a real fight.

Sandy by now was worried. He stepped in to try to stop the fight, but one of Cunningham's men pulled out a knife and thrust it into his heart, killing him instantly. As he slipped to the ground, Anne's screams froze everyone into still silence.

Patrick turned in fury on Cunningham, ready to kill him. Then Barbara stepped forward out of the crowd and grabbed his arm with her claw-like hand. 'Wait! Would ye kill yer own father?' she cried, before clutching at her chest and slipping to the ground like a pile of old rags, gasping her last breath.

Was it Barbara who had taken Patrick from his father at the fair all those years ago out of revenge for her dead brother, father, husband and sons, and carried him south until leaving him with the comatose Sandy? It is likely that she did, and then, ultimately, she made amends by saving her enemy's life.

And so, Cunningham had found his long lost son. Anne, after many tears for her father, married Patrick, who eventually inherited Cunningham's farm over the head of his cousin, thereby sparking off yet one more feud.

But that's another story ...

Memories of a Cullercoats Fishwife

'My first vivid memory is of New Year's morning, 1861. I was sitting on a "proggy" [rag] mat in front of the range, and for once the whole family were crowded into our one small room because the weather outside was really terrible. Even the window shutters were closed, which was very rare. Then, the front door flew open and Uncle Jack came in on a blast of wind, covered in snow, shouting for me da.

"Tommy, there's a collier brig off Tynemouth in trouble, an' I don't know how we'll get to it 'cos we'll nivvor get the lifeboat out in that sea!"

I was swept up into me mother's shawl, and the whole lot of us bundled out of the door and down the road to the headland.

I could see the fishing cobles lined up safe, pulled clear of the beach in the little bay below, but it was more difficult to see anything beyond the huge waves and the white, hissing spray, crashing high over the rocks. Then I saw it! The brig was being tossed about offshore like a cork, with its sails all torn into rags.

Me da ran to help the other men and some of the women with the lifeboat, but instead of hauling it down the slope into the sea, they were harnessing horses to it, and pulling it around to face the opposite direction.

I didn't see any more after that, 'cos me ma ran home with me and left me with Ganny, my grandmother, before running back to join the others.

It was dark when they all returned, and instead of chattering loudly as they usually did, they all just stripped off their soaking outer clothes and fell exhausted onto their pallets to sleep.

Years later, the story of that night became quite famous. The *Lovely Nellie* had been bound for London with a load of coal, and the storm had blown her off course. She found it impossible to enter the Tyne for shelter, so she struggled northwards past Cullercoats with the idea to drive ashore at Whitley sands, but she failed and was wrecked on the rocks three-quarters of a mile offshore. All the men and women and older children from Cullercoats helped to drag the lifeboat overland for three miles up the coast in those terrible conditions. Then the men rowed out to the ship, where the crew were by this time clinging on to the rigging for dear life as the waves were breaking over the decks. Our men managed to save all of the crew, except for one seaman and a little cabin boy who fell from the mast into the sea and drowned.

An artist called John Charlton painted the scene in 1910. He called the picture *The Women*.

Lots of artists visited Cullercoats because they found the little bay with its many fishing cobles and all the characters hereabouts and their little houses so picturesque. My neighbour Maggie was painted a few times by Winslow Homer, who I've heard is America's greatest artist!

All these strange art people might have thought us quaint, but I wonder if they appreciated just how hard we all had to work! We had to be tough.

Me ma started training me early. Before I was half grown, I often went down with her at first light to meet the boats returning from fishing. When me da and me two eldest brothers had handed over the catch, they went home to bed and we sorted the fish on the beach – there was always plenty of herring in those days, along with cod, haddock, whiting and turbot – and we would cut off the heads then pack them head to tail in the wicker baskets (we called them 'creels') to get more in. Ma's creel weighed about eight stone when it was full, and she had permanent marks on her shoulders where the straps dug in. My creel was less than half that size, but it was still heavy for me.

Then we would trudge up the hill with the other fisherlassies and we'd go selling. We'd walk for miles and miles around the villages and towns, visiting old customers and new and filleting the fish with sharp knives and cold hands. We would shout, "Buy fee-s-ch" until my throat was hoarse. I soon got used to that though and I started my own round when I was twelve years old.

When me ma and I weren't selling fish, we were searching for bait, either digging for sandworms or gathering mussels, limpets and dog-crabs from the rocks. Then we helped me da and me brothers to bait the hundreds of hooks on the fishing lines, which was a task needing experienced fingers otherwise there would be lots of blood and not much progress. On a Sunday, me da spread the fishing nets out over the ground and we would all help with the mending.

In the evenings, we washed our creels and stacked them in the back lane along with the lobster pots and wooden barrels of salt for the herring. Then we dunked our clothes in a pail of water and scrubbed them, and hung them to drip before draping them over the fender; of course they were never dry the next day, so we had at least one spare set.

All us lassies wore the same style: on the top was a serviceable jacket known as a "bedgoon", and over that we wore a black or dark grey, fringed shawl crossed over at the front and tucked in at the back waist. The skirt was always dark blue or black flannel, with the hem above the ankle and lots of tucks going around from the hem up – the more the better, to keep our legs warm in the winter. To protect the skirt we wore an apron, and we used a wad of paper to protect our backs from the water leaking out of the creels. When we weren't barefoot on the beach, we wore black knitted stockings and strong shoes. The older women wore black straw bonnets. Us young-uns just went bare headed most of the time, but we had to tie our hair right back otherwise it got tangled and full of fish scales.

There was never enough fresh water at the end of the day to wash ourselves as well as the clothes, so we mostly washed in the cold sea. Then when we were clean, we prepared bread for the next day, cooked our meal of herring and "tatties", and then knitted till it was time for bed. Ma would often light up her clay tobacco pipe and sit on a cracket by the front door in the long summer evenings if it was fine, and I would meet up with some of the other girls to go for a stroll along the cliffs and have a banter with the lads.

I particularly liked John. I had known him all me life, but when I was 16 I noticed what a fine, well-built lad he'd turned out to be. Before that, I'd always felt a bit sorry for him 'cos his father and two older brothers had been lost while out at sea fishin' when he was just a little 'un, and the family always struggled after that. But ours is a close community, and the men all took him under their wing. He worked hard and managed to get himself a boat, and, well, when he asked if we could be married, I accepted like a shot. Aye, we had 60 happy years together and 12 kids with nine survivin', so we didn't do so bad.

The young men have always picked girls from their own community to wed, because we're used to the hard work and the cold sea air. Girls from outside don't survive; they're a burden rather than a help to their husbands.

Many's the time I've gone down to the beach to help John and the lads launch the coble in the dark, paying no mind to the long day of work behind me and the long day ahead. I would watch the little red, square sail disappear into the gloom, and then I'd be down there again at dawn along with the other women for their return, looking for the pattern of light shining from the coal-fired brazier which distinguished John's boat from all the rest.

Life was made a bit easier for our generation of fisherlassies with the coming of the railway to Cullercoats in 1864. It meant we were able to catch the morning train to take our fish the 10 miles up to Newcastle, or even further – over to the colliery towns in Co Durham, or up the Tyne Valley. But then, when the electric train started shortly after 1900, there was an unholy row. We were banned from some of the trains because they said that the water dripping from the creels flowed into the first-class compartments and caused a smell! My friend Nannie said at a meeting with the railway officials, "They're tellin' lees when they say that. Thor's nee dreep from the creels. The dreep comes from the boxes." She and Long Betty and the rest of us made such a fuss that the officials went away with their tails between their legs.

The trains brought lots of visitors; in fact the village became quite a fashionable resort, which meant we could sell our crabs, lobsters and winkles, or "williks" as we called them, from the doorways of our cottages at weekends. This was just as well, because there weren't so many fish in the sea by then. Way back in 1750, Cullercoats, with its natural harbour, had been known as the best fish market in the North of England, but by 1900 steam trawlers were catching most of the fish and taking it to North Shields; increasingly we had to tramp over there to get our fish, for our husbands were finding it harder and harder to land a decent catch.

Fishing was always a dangerous business. The terrible loss of life always affected my John badly, with him remembering his early tragedy, and he was often out with the lifeboat. I worried about him all the time he was out. Whenever I could I collected money for the lifeboat. My friend Polly Donkin collected over £1,000 for the RNLI and in 1931 she was invited to meet the Prince of Wales in London to collect a gold brooch for "distinguished services". She wore her best, coloured silk shawl and a black and white print apron for the occasion, and when she met the Prince, she said of him, "He's a real homely lad."

She was 73 then, the same age as me, and we were still both working. I remember her words the day she retired.

"Aa's put me creel away. It's hingin' up i' the wash-hoose noo, an' wor Donkin says he'll born it if Aa try to get oot wi'd agyen."

She died last year in March 1951, aged 93, and she was carried around Cullercoats in a procession for her "last trip". It's traditional! I hope they'll do the same for me.

There's talk that they're goin' to pull down our little cottages, which is a great pity. When they go, and when I go, I hope folk will nivvor forget the bonny Fishwives of Cullercoats. Aye, I have some grand memories!'

The Curse of the Outrageous Delavals

On a crisp December afternoon in 1752, Captain Francis Blake Delaval stood at the top of the broad stone steps at the back of Seaton Delaval Hall, swaying slightly, a glass of claret in his hand. Letting his gaze travel southwards over the manicured gardens and the lonely obelisk towards distant Tynemouth, he thought about his young seafaring days and tried to forget his continually nagging worries. How different his life would have been had his uncle, the Admiral, not left him this place.

His life had not been easy, and he knew that, at 60, he was starting to look the worse for wear; but he had always done his duty. He congratulated himself that he had fathered eight sons and three daughters, which wasn't bad considering that the Delaval name had previously been dying out. Yes, thanks to him, from now on the family's name and fortune would prosper.

He was wrong on both counts.

Another sip of claret and a step forward brought the Captain's heavy body crashing down the steps to the bottom, his leg snapping as he fell, with the sickening crack of a bull-whip. A loud bellow brought the shocked servants out to carry him inside. A few days afterwards, he was dead.

His eldest son and heir, Francis, known as Frank, was now free to carelessly bring the family almost to its knees, gaining for it the reputation as being one of the wildest, unluckiest and most extravagant families of the 18th century.

Originally, the Delavals came to England with William the Conqueror. They settled in what was then the ancient manor of Hartley; but by 1718 they were saddled with debts and were forced to put the 6,500 acre estate up for sale.

Admiral George Delaval, a middle-aged man from a different branch of the family, who had made a huge fortune, decided to buy the estate for himself. He commissioned the famous architect Sir John Vanbrugh to design a great palatial mansion to replace the existing crumbling old manor house. With no expense spared, the new house was to comprise a centre block between two ornate wings, situated in a peaceful setting half a mile inland from the cold sea winds and the bustling, grimy family businesses – coalmines, glassworks, farms and saltpans – at Seaton Sluice. The spectacular view from the front stretched up the sand-dune fringed coastline and over the Northumberland coastal plain to the distant hills.

Unfortunately, before the beautiful new building was completed, the Admiral was thrown off his horse and, his foot caught in the stirrup, he was dragged over several fields before being deposited, dead, in view of the Hall, where the obelisk now stands.

His favourite nephew, Captain Francis Blake Delaval, was at that time making his career at sea, and it was to him, in 1723, that the Admiral left the Delaval estate. But the young naval captain was less than ecstatic. Despite the fact that the house when it was completed was a masterpiece of elegance, he viewed it as a white elephant and he had a huge construction bill to pay, which he could not afford. Fortunately, he married a rich heiress, Rhoda Apreece, from Huntingdonshire, and then he inherited the two Northumberland estates of Dissington and Ford Castle, so his money worries appeared to be over.

Captain Delaval's children, in particular the eldest, Frank, grew to be good-looking, extrovert, noisy and wilful. They all loved entertaining, play-acting and practical jokes.

Frank was irresistible to most people. He was outstandingly handsome and well built, generous, amiable and full of vitality. But his extraordinary extravagance and his relentless pursuit of pleasure were soon chipping away at the family's fortune. He started to spend most of his time in London surrounded by a circle of corrupt theatrical friends, and his scandalous behaviour became the talk of the town. He was head over heels in debt and his worried father deliberately kept him short of funds.

When Frank was 22, in 1749, Francis' recently widowed cousin brought her ward, 18-year-old Miss Betty Roach, to stay at Seaton Delaval. Betty's upbringing in France had been unusual and she was wild, raven-haired and barely able to speak English. She fell for Frank immediately, and almost as quickly he seduced her.

Captain Delaval at this time was morose and drinking heavily, and neither he nor his wife Rhoda liked Betty Roach. So, when Frank ended his visit home and returned to London, Betty followed him, and he set up house for her in Soho, to be his mistress.

Frank's debts escalated. He and his friends were seriously in need of funds. There was only one thing to do, and that was for Frank to marry for money. Believing her to be worth a fortune, he married in 1750 the monstrously fat and extremely plain, middle-aged and intellectually challenged Lady Isabella Pawlett. Imagine his horror when he learned that she was worth a tiny fraction of what he had been led to believe.

As soon as Lady Isabella was ensconced in Seaton Delaval Hall, Frank continued his life as if she did not exist. He thought about building a house for his mistresses to live in while he was at home, and he happened to mention the notion to his notorious and disruptive friend Samuel Foote, who bet him 100 guineas that he could not build it in a day. Of course, Frank took him on. He gathered together all the materials and workmen, and within 24 hours, Starlight Castle was erected on the north bank of Hollywell Dene on the Delaval estate. A ruin now, it resembled a small castle, and got its name because teams of builders toiled on it through the night.

Frank's excesses continued. He spent lavishly to hire Drury Lane Theatre for one night so that he, his family and friends could stage their own version of *Othello*. The whole of London society scrambled to the performance, including royalty; and the House of Commons even closed two hours early so that the politicians could attend.

It was six months later when his poor father, the Captain, worried about the influence of his wayward son on the family and its dwindling fortune, fell so disastrously down the Seaton Delaval steps.

Two months after his father's death, Frank held a huge banquet at the Hall. He loved practical jokes, subjecting his guests to all kinds of humility and hilarity. There were competitions where the men were urged to bite the heads off live sparrows. At night, beds would collapse, dunking their occupants into tanks of cold water; false walls would fall down, and dead animals were hidden in the sheets.

The second Delaval son, John, enjoyed a party as much as his brother, but he had a more sensible head on his shoulders. Now that his father was dead, he realised that he could not stand by and watch Frank ruin the family businesses.

Frank had no interest in commerce, fancying his chances instead of becoming an MP, in which position he could not be arrested for debt. He stood for election at Andover in 1754 and won by buying votes and firing 500 guineas from a cannon at his election address. John was also elected in as MP for Berwick.

John and Frank came to an arrangement where John would look after the businesses with Edward, the third eldest brother, and Frank would relinquish the estates in return for an allowance, to which he readily agreed.

Meanwhile, Frank had lost interest in his former mistress Betty Roach, who had borne him a son and a daughter and who was now continually asking him for money. His marriage to Isabella had been dissolved and he had taken up with a beautiful actress, Miss Ann Catley, a woman of expensive tastes, who also went on to have his child.

Increasingly, Frank's creditors were hounding him, and it seemed to him that his only escape would be to join the Grenadier Guards and take part in the Seven Years' War, the battle between Britain and France for overseas supremacy. Never one to be in the background, he was the first man to wade ashore on a windswept beach near St Malo in the face of anticipated French opposition, but in fact the beach was empty and there were no French soldiers in sight. Tales of his bravery multiplied out of all proportion and he was hailed as a hero, gaining him a knighthood.

His youngest brothers were not so lucky. Robert and Henry, both professional soldiers, died in battle, George was drowned at sea, Ralph was killed in an earthquake and Tom, who had industriously improved the Seaton Sluice harbour and run the glassworks, was later killed in a fall from his horse in Hyde Park.

Frank's last outburst of extravagance, despite his soaring debts, was the addition of a magnificent stable wing to the Hall. By this time, at the age of 41, he had become grossly overweight, coarse of face and careless in his dress. He died three years later in 1771, after eating a large meal of venison and drinking himself into a state where he could forget the ever-present problem of his huge debts.

The prodigious funeral, arranged by brother Edward, was massively expensive, much to the fury of the new head of the family. John was mortgaged up to the hilt, Frank's creditors were knocking on the door and everyone, including his two surviving wayward sisters, seemed to be asking him for money. Still in mourning for his 19-year-old daughter Rhoda who had died the previous year of consumption, he was resolved to protect his only son and heir, Jack, from the influences of the outside world, which in his opinion had corrupted his brother Frank. However, three years later, Jack became ill with consumption. He was sent to Bristol for the healing waters, but the next year, at the age of 20, he died. Ironically, consumption was not the cause, but, in the fashion of his late uncle Frank, he died as a result of a kick in the testicles delivered by an irate laundry maid.

And so, what appeared to be a curse on the male members of the Delaval family drew to a close. Lord John, as he became, died at the age of 81, and his brother Edward, the last legitimate male of the family, inherited the Seaton estate.

In the end, a daughter came to the fore, as Seaton Delaval eventually passed to the son of Rhoda Delaval, the eldest daughter of Captain Francis Blake Delaval. The beautiful house was engulfed in flames in 1822 and many treasures were lost; but it is still possible to look at Seaton Delaval Hall and imagine it in the days of the outrageous, party-loving Delavals.

The Body in the Bank

The Royal Arcade at the foot of Pilgrim Street, Newcastle was one of the earliest developments undertaken by Richard Grainger, the building genius who went on to transform the city from a brick and timber shambles into an architectural masterpiece. It was also the scene, six years after it was built, of a brutal and mysterious murder, which would be the source of controversy for decades to come.

At about 2 o'clock in the morning on 7th December 1838, smoke was seen to be pouring out of the window of the Savings Bank, which was alongside the entrance to the Arcade. The fire brigade, whose headquarters was situated only 200 yards away, was quickly alerted and the fire, which was found to be just a small affair, was soon extinguished.

When the firemen entered the bank and made their way through the waiting room to the office beyond, they found that the door was partially blocked as if someone on the other side was preventing them from opening it. More force was brought to bear, and this time the door opened with no obstruction whatsoever.

Groping their way through the smoke-filled room, the firemen stumbled over something lying on the floor. A lantern was brought to the object, and in the glimmering light they saw the body of a grey-haired man, lying face down on the blood-soaked hearthrug, with his head beaten almost to a pulp. By his side was a bent poker, which was obviously the murder weapon as it was covered with blood and hair. The victim's pockets were stuffed full of coal and paper, which led the firemen to believe that the fire had been started deliberately to hide the evidence of the murder.

The firemen continued searching the room, and in a corner they found another man, lying apparently unconscious. No blood was on that part of the floor where he lay. The man opened his eyes immediately on discovery, and then he shut them again, creating a suspicion that he was shamming. He had a small cut on his throat, and was suffering partly from the effects of the smoke, but otherwise there was nothing seriously the matter with him. He identified himself as Archibald Bolam, the holder of the important position of actuary in the bank.

To all outward appearances, 41-year-old Archibald Bolam was a thoroughly trustworthy and honest man. He had been born at

Harbottle, Coquetdale, and from humble beginnings he raised himself to the position of schoolmaster at Holystone. He then moved to Newcastle to work in the Percy Street Academy, at which time he became a respected member of the Presbyterian Church, before securing the appointment of actuary to the Savings Bank.

The murder victim was Joseph Millie, a mildly amiable and pleasant man. Born in North Shields, he had succeeded his father in an old-established ironmongery business but had failed to make it pay. For years he did odd jobs to pay off his creditors, then, at the age of 56, in the March preceding his murder, he secured the job of occasional clerk in the Savings Bank.

Archibald Bolam had taken a shine to Millie. He suddenly turned against his highly respected and able assistant clerk Mr George Ridley, who was working for him at the time, and he managed to get him dismissed from his post, replacing him with the unfortunate Millie on 5th December, two days before the murder.

The inquest on Millie was opened in the afternoon some 12 hours after the murder, at the Blue Posts, a hostelry on Pilgrim Street. News of the tragedy had spread, and the street in front of the old inn was packed with excited crowds.

Bolam gave his account of the occurrence to the magistrates. He stated that he had been receiving a series of threatening letters from an unknown person, the last of which had been slipped under the bank door on the evening previous to the murder. He had left the bank and gone to his home in Gateshead, leaving no one on the premises, but that night, after worrying about the letters, he had returned to the bank. He said he had found the bank door as he had left it; but on entering the office he saw Millie lying on the hearthrug. Believing Millie was asleep, he proceeded to his desk, but then a man with a blackened face had appeared and struck him a blow on the right temple. A desperate struggle had ensued, and Bolam claimed that his attacker had attempted to slit his throat, at which time he had passed out.

This account of events as he told it sounded unlikely and inconsistent and was full of contradictions. The firemen told of their suspicions. A doctor stated that the throat wound had probably been self-inflicted, tying in with the police's account of a small quantity of blood, which had been found on Bolam's desk together with a bloodstained paper knife.

A verdict of 'Wilful murder against Archibald Bolam' was returned, and the prisoner was sent for trial at the Spring Assizes.

Strong feeling against Bolam escalated in Newcastle, exacerbated by the suspicion that he had powerful friends who would prevent justice from being done. The trial was postponed until the end of July 1839, when it became necessary to take strict precautions for the protection of the prisoner from the mob on his journey between the gaol and the courts.

A series of revelations had emerged since the murder to suggest that Bolam was not the pillar of respectability that he claimed to be, so it was no surprise that his trial at the Guildhall was packed to capacity.

The bank porter gave evidence that he had left Bolam and Millie sitting together 'like brothers' at half-past three on the afternoon of the murder. Millie was never to see his wife or his home in Croft Stairs again. Bolam, however, was seen returning home to Gateshead, and a neighbour heard breaking glass, as if he had entered his house by a rear window.

The judge and the jury now began to hear of Bolam's double life. It emerged that the accused man had huge gambling debts, and that he had quarrelled with his Presbyterian friends over his frequent visits to 'vice dens'. His housekeeper, Mary Ann Walker, a lady of known 'ill repute', who was also his mistress, admitted that she had sponged the sleeve of the coat that Bolam had been wearing, where a close examination afterwards revealed bloodstains and smears.

The prosecution theorised that, after a sudden quarrel, Bolam had beaten out Millie's brains. Afterwards, he had gone home, where he had been cleaned up by his housekeeper before returning to the bank to set fire to it and destroy the evidence. After being caught in the act, he had concocted the story of the disguised murderer.

However, the evidence was purely circumstantial, added to which there was no satisfactory motive, as the two men were known to have been on amicable terms that day. Nor did the bank admit to any irregularities in their accounts, which Millie might have uncovered.

Most people believed that Bolam was guilty and should hang. The judge, Mr Justice Maul, was more sceptical. He summed up favourably for the prisoner, and the jury brought in a verdict of manslaughter. Archibald Bolam was sentenced to transportation for life to Australia.

The scene of the crime, Richard Grainger's elegant Royal Arcade in Pilgrim Street, eventually fell into decline and was dismantled in the mid 1970s, to be replaced by the present Swan House.

But we had not heard the last of our supposed murderer. A sundial can be seen in the Botanical Gardens in Sydney, presented by one Archibald Bolam, 'one time citizen of Newcastle upon Tyne'. And in the graveyard of St Stephen's church in Sydney is a tombstone with the inscription, 'Sacred to the memory of Archibald Bolam, who died 25th December, 1862, aged 67 years,' ending with the words, 'Here lies an honest man.'

Spirited Away

A drop (or several) of the 'hard stuff' has long been a welcome, or in some cases essential, way of spiriting away the cares of the day. Many would risk their lives, and many have, to enjoy their favourite tipple.

This was never so true as in the late 18th and early 19th centuries when the prices of whisky, brandy and gin, previously cheap enough for most to enjoy, more than doubled. The government levied huge taxes on all luxuries in order to finance the expensive French wars; consequently prices rocketed, and smuggling became a way for the adventurous working man to make some money while at the same time easing his resentment by thumbing his nose at authority.

All along the rugged Northumberland coastline gangs of smugglers operated in secluded coves under cover of darkness. The stakes were huge. Fortunes could be made, but for those who were caught and convicted, the penalty was usually the gallows.

Excise officers, called 'gaugers', were stationed, in couples for their own safety, at likely smuggling routes to search every passing carrier's cart for smuggled goods. Often outwitted, and sometimes murdered, it was not an enviable job.

The wild border country was rife with smuggling, and the fishing village of Spittal, just south of Berwick, was particularly notorious. The fishermen, smugglers all, were expert in landing forbidden contraband, usually gin, from the Dutch luggers, which anchored just off shore. Their houses contained secret hiding places in walls, lofts and under floors. The fisherwomen of Berwick would carry containers full of spirits under their voluminous skirts into town, smiling innocently if they encountered any watching customs officers.

One determined smuggler who gained notoriety for his daring deeds was Alley Geggie, from a tribe of outlaws living in Coldstream just north of the border. He was a broad-shouldered, powerful man with the borderer's characteristic quick wit and granite constitution.

On one of Geggie's many smuggling expeditions, he headed for Boulmer, a remote seaside village and renowned smuggling centre just north of Alnmouth, where he and several partners in crime had arranged a rendezvous with the Boulmer fishermen and a ship from Holland.

On arrival at his destination at dusk, Geggie headed for a secluded hollow near the shoreline where he tied up his horse and a heavier cob, which he had been leading for the transportation of the kegs, and then he crept watchfully through the scrubby bushes to join the other waiting men.

All was quiet except for the gentle beat of the waves and the rustling of the long grass in the chill October breeze. Then, through the gloom of the darkening night, the brown sail of a Dutch lugger appeared around the headland. Immediately the sound of many whispering voices broke the silence, and all hands scurried onto the beach to launch two small boats, manned by skilled oarsmen.

Stealth and speed were essential now. Kegs of prime gin were expertly landed on the beach and lifted onto waiting carts.

Geggie had loaded two kegs onto his cob when suddenly a gunshot tore through the night and men were shouting and running for their lives from the beach. He cursed roundly. Unwilling to part with his ill-gotten gains, and gambling he had not been seen, he led his two horses quietly through the darkness for about a mile along a scrubby track until he reached the junction with the main track north.

Just as he was congratulating himself on his escape, two gaugers armed with pistols and cutlasses appeared on the track in front of him. In the pale moonlight he recognised one of them as an old adversary and constant thorn in his side. 'Well, Alley Geggie, we've got you this time,' the officer gloated. 'We'll take possession of those goods, if you please, and take you prisoner.'

At first Geggie said and did nothing, his mind working. Then, he slapped the cob hard on the rump, sending it trotting away down the road. The younger of the two gaugers immediately turned to capture the evidence and Geggie's apprehender dismounted – this was foolish, as he was head and shoulders smaller than the smuggler. Within a minute, the excise man was knocked to the ground and Geggie was galloping north towards the border, furious at losing his two casks of gin and his best cob.

Late the next day, Geggie had stopped in a wood near the ferry over the River Tweed in order to give his horse a rest. Always alert, while watching the road below he saw the two gaugers riding wearily by, obviously determined to track him down. The annoyance that at first clouded his face turned to a crooked smile as his sense of humour was triggered by an ingenious plan.

Quickly, he ran through a short cut to the cottage of the ferryman, who happened to owe him for several 'grey hens' (stoneware bottles) of gin.

Soon after, the two weary officials knocked on the cottage door and asked the ferryman if he had seen a person answering Geggie's description.

'Aye, such a man has just been kented across,' said the boatman.

The pursuers then requested to be conveyed over also, and they were told to go down to the ferry landing.

A heavily cloaked, bent figure stood by the boat. He took the passengers' fares and he watched them step on board. Then, remaining himself on the shore, he gave the boat an almighty push into the fast-flowing river. As the boat was borne swiftly downstream with its bewildered occupants, Geggie threw off his cloak, drew himself up to his full height and shouted after them, 'Now, damn ye, aw'm Alley Geggie!'

The boat drifted for well over a mile towards Berwick before the unfortunate excise men, using their arms, managed to paddle it ashore. They never did catch the notorious Alley Geggie.

* * * * * * * * * * * * * *

While daredevil desperados like Geggie were busy running foreign spirits from coast to customer, others were cheating the excise men by manufacturing and selling their own 'innocent whisky'.

One such outlaw was a Highlander named Donald McDonald, who had been forced to flee over the border from his native Scotland to settle in the remote Cheviot Hills at Upper Coquetdale. Here, illicit distilleries were numerous and due to the inaccessibility of this area, smuggling activities went on almost unchallenged by the gaugers. The barley required for the manufacture of the 'real mountain dew' was carted in open daylight from the lower parts of the valley, and peat was openly cut near the 'stills'.

Donald McDonald chose a lonely spot near a burn, where he built a rough, windowless hut with wood, turf and rushes to house himself and his working equipment. In the centre he set up a small coarse table with two chairs, and beside the doorway he placed a bench. His bed, in the corner, was a pile of dried bracken, of which there was a plentiful supply on the surrounding hills.

Donald soon built up a fine reputation for his whisky and his generosity. Consequently, he was never short of business or of visitors.

One afternoon, a man called at the hut and Donald, in his usual hospitable way, asked the visitor to sit down and he brought him bread, cheese, an earthen pot of water, two glasses and a large jug of his 'prime stuff'. While they chatted, the stranger's arrogant manner made Donald suspicious, and, taking his glass, he went to sit on the bench by the door, knowing that his slight frame was no match for the other man's obvious strength should he have to defend himself.

'Donald McDonald,' said the stranger, 'you distil smuggled whisky and I am an Excise officer. I came here to make you a prisoner.'

Donald tried his best to persuade the gauger to let him go free, but the man insisted he would do his duty.

'Fery severe! Fery hard indeed!' said Donald. 'I deen't want te quarrel wi' yer honour, but I'm no' just willin' to be taken. Did onybody see ye come in?'

'Not a soul,' replied the officer, rising from his seat.

'Then neebody shall see ye gan oot!' thundered the Highlander, his face turning ugly, 'And if ye finger either sword or pistol, yer blood be on yer own heed.' He took a brace of pistols from behind the door and cocked them, leaving the gauger no alternative but to sit down again and, eventually, resume eating and drinking.

By sunset, the whisky in the jug had been consumed and the unwelcome visitor had rolled off to sleep on the bracken bed in the corner. Donald then went to work moving all his belongings and his distillery to a safe place, using his enemy's horse.

When the excise man awoke in the early morning, with a monumental hangover, he was alone in the empty cottage. Then, finding his horse had gone, he started the long walk homewards.

Later that day, he returned with a force of men to search for Donald. All he found was his horse, weary and without its bridle, and an empty, upended cask upon which was written the words, 'SEARCH IN VAIN'.

The Witches
of
Alnwick

The people of Alnwick can proudly boast that their lively market town has been voted one of the best places to live in England. With its magnificent castle, beautiful surrounding countryside and strong community spirit, it is easy to see why. But in the 17th century, things were very different. The streets were filled with foul-smelling rubbish, the castle was a battered fortress falling into disrepair, the countryside was rough and poor, and the community was steeped in superstition and fear.

This was the century of witchcraft hysteria throughout Europe, linked to the rise of the reformed Church and its fundamentalist approach to the Bible, which states in Exodus XXII, verse 18, 'Thou shalt not suffer a witch to live'. The ducking stool, used now with much hilarity at the colourful annual Alnwick Fair, then had a more sinister entertainment value, whereby suspected witches were tried and ducked until they often drowned.

In 1646 it was published, 'Every old woman with a wrinkled face, a furrowed brow, a hairy lip, a gobber tooth, a squint eye, a squeaking voice, a scolding tongue … is not only suspected but pronounced a witch.' Over three thousand 'witches' were officially executed in England during this period. Life was difficult enough for any woman who was old and poor, but if she offended anyone, either intentionally or otherwise, she could find herself accused of being a witch and facing a horrible death.

One such woman was Annie, who lived at Shilbottle, a small village four miles to the south of Alnwick.

One evening in 1611, Annie's daughter Esther came home in a state of distress, bruised all over her face and body and her clothes torn to shreds. She had been assaulted by a farmer's son from Alnwick.

Annie's husband was a seafarer, rarely at home, so it was left to Annie herself to track down and confront the attacker. This she did,

but the young man laughed in her face, saying that Esther had been willing, but because he had not paid her enough she had turned nasty and he had only been defending himself. Annie was furious. She knew her gentle daughter and she had no doubt that this man was lying. But how could justice be done? It was useless to approach the male authorities of the town, as assault of this kind was commonplace and not considered to be a crime of any significance.

But Annie had women friends who could identify with Esther's experience, and who welcomed the opportunity for revenge. They found out that the young man was working in a field at nearby High Buston, and five of them went to confront him.

The arrogance of the man whipped up the women's fury. He laughed at their accusations, making lewd comments and seemingly enjoying the attention. He had not noticed that Annie had started a fire in the corner of the field. At a nod from her, the women grabbed him and wrestled him to the ground. While he lay there, they stripped him of his trousers, and Annie approached with a red-hot iron bar. He screamed that his uncle was a local magistrate and that they would pay dearly for hurting him. Then he laughed, thinking they were bluffing. His screams returned when Annie placed the sizzling poker into his groin.

The man survived, although unable to repeat his criminal inclinations against women. He had many enemies and consequently kept the incident to himself lest he be ridiculed. Fear of witches was mounting at this time, and he took advantage of this to spread rumours about Annie.

The next Alnwick Fair day, he and his friends denounced Annie as a witch, and the crowd, fuelled by ale and eager for some entertainment from the newly installed ducking stool, called for her to be tried there and then. The local magistrate had no choice but to agree for fear of a riot.

Poor Annie was tied to the wooden stool, which was poised, at the end of a levering arm, over a large vat of water that had been drawn from the River Aln. She was ducked once, then twice, but the third time, greatly weakened, she drowned in the filthy water. The theory that water would reject a witch proved that Annie was innocent, and when attempts to revive her failed, too late, she was pronounced 'not guilty'.

* * * * * * * * * * * * *

At a time when only the richest could afford doctors, most people relied on herbs and potions supplied by 'charmers', who were mainly female. This meant that a woman innocently attempting to ease suffering could be arrested for witchcraft.

This was the fate of an elderly 'charmer' called Margaret Stothard, who lived in the tiny village of Edlingham, six miles south-west of Alnwick. She was credited with many extraordinary powers. Her trial took place on 22nd January 1683, and the charges against her were laid before Mr Henry Ogle, the local Justice of the Peace.

The first witness against Margaret was John Mills, who had the tenancy of Edlingham Castle, a fortified manor house dating from the 12th century. The preserved castle ruins stand near the head of a valley formed by a tributary of the River Aln, surrounded by lonely moorland. His evidence suggests that he was probably of a nervous disposition and subject to fits. He testified: 'One Sunday night lying in bed I did hear a great blast of wind go by the window, then something fell like a great weight on my heart and gave a great cry like a cat. When this was ended there appeared a light at the foot of my bed, and in this light I did recognise Margaret Stothard. For a time my speech was taken from me. When I'd recovered the power to speak, I cried out, "The Witch, The Witch."'

John Mills said he was so hysterical that his family had to fetch his brother to hold him down. The same happened several times, always beginning with a blast of wind. To prevent the hair on his head from standing 'on end upwards', he said he had to jump out of bed, light a candle and read his bible. He stated that when he passed Margaret's door in order to pay the landlord his rent, a flash of fire came over him and his horse would not move. He was so afraid when he got home that he had to have his brothers and neighbours to stay.

The next witness was William Collingwood of Edlingham. He testified that eight years earlier a neighbour, Jane Carr, had told him of the time she called Margaret Stothard to cure her sick child. Margaret had put her mouth to the child's mouth, 'chirping and sucking' as if drawing out the heart from the chest, then she sat on a stone in the doorway and 'raved', which frightened the woman and the child. When she went away, a little calf tied up outside the house went mad and had to be killed. It was thought that the calf had taken on the 'distemper'.

Jacob Mills, possibly John's brother, who was now living at the castle, added another indictment. He stated that eight years previously, Margaret had called at the house of Alexander Nickle of Lorbottle and his wife, asking for food. The wife did not give her anything, and Margaret had waved a white cloth three times as she went away. A child in the house then grew unwell, crying out about the 'white thing' pressing on her like a brick to her back and saying it would 'press out my heart'. The child died the next day, and the father, on consulting the well-respected Lady Widdrington, was told that as the child was not suffering from any illness, she must have been bewitched.

The last recorded evidence was from Isobel Maine, a spinster from nearby Shawdon. She claimed to have consulted Margaret when the cows produced sour milk. Margaret told her 'ill eyes' had looked on it. Isobel asked why the cows sweated when they stood in the byre, and Margaret suggested rubbing their backs with salt and water and always to put a little salt in the milking pail. The milk improved and butter and cheese were soon back in production. Margaret had not asked for any payment for this service, so the accusation seems mean-spirited in the extreme.

Old Margaret must have been shaking when the Justice of the Peace considered his verdict. With no pension and no other means of support, she had managed to exist by using her wits and trying to help people, and now she faced the death penalty. Luckily for her, Henry Ogle was a sensible, compassionate man aware of many past injustices, and he found her not guilty.

It seems that Margaret was not hunted to death after her trial, as was the fate of so many accused witches. She was one of the lucky few.

Dickie
of
Kingswood

Around the beginning of the 18th century, Dickie of Kingswood, as he was popularly known, resided in the ancient ruins of Starward Pele, about nine miles to the west of Hexham.

Dickie was a thief. Thieving was in his blood. He came from a long line of Border Reivers who rode across Northumberland's difficult, remote terrain taking cattle and horses and anything else they could lay their hands on, and transporting them back to their lairs over paths known only to themselves. Those days were gone, stamped out since the unification of the crowns a century earlier; but law and order was hard to enforce in a place with so many hidden places of refuge.

Starward Pele, used in the 14th century as an easily defendable stronghold for people and animals in case of invasion, stands on a small platform at the end of a pear-shaped promontory, which is joined to the mainland by a narrow ridge flanked on both sides by precipitous ravines. The River Allen and its tributary the Harsingdale Burn run at its base, the whole area being densely covered by conifers and pines and known as Kingswood. A more impregnable and hidden position could scarcely be found; and this suited Dickie very well.

Unlike his forbears, Dickie was not a violent man. His boast was that, though he was afraid of no man, he never had, and never would, dip his hand in a man's blood. Thieving to him was very much a battle of wits; and he was good at it, due in no small part to his natural roguish charm and a way of talking himself out of trouble.

One bright autumn morning, Dickie set out on foot from Starward Pele and headed east towards the outskirts of Newcastle where he was hopeful of some rich pickings. Sure enough, after a pleasant 25 mile stroll, he spied a pair of fat white oxen in a field adjoining a farmhouse in Denton Burn. He resolved that, if he could do it without too much trouble, he would have them.

He rested under a hedge until dark, after which time he entered the field and skilfully drove the placid animals off into the night.

His plan was to drive them west; but first he headed along the rutted, muddy road north, leaving an obvious trail to put the farmer on a false scent should he set out in pursuit of his prize beasts.

After a few miles, Dickie made the turn westwards to travel across country, pleased with himself and his booty and without a care in the world.

Four days later, he reached Lanercost, just over the county border in Cumberland. There, an old farmer riding a strikingly good-looking chestnut mare stopped to pass the time of day.

'By, them's fine beasts,' the old man said admiringly.

'My pride and joy,' said Dickie, quickly adopting a sad expression, 'but I've fallen on hard times and I know where I can get a good price for them.'

'I'll give ye a better price,' the farmer offered, casting a shrewd, practiced eye over the rippling muscles of the oxen. 'Come to the hoose for a sup and we can talk business.'

Dickie accompanied him to the farmhouse where the pair struck a deal over a bottle of whisky. He pocketed the money and patted his pocket thoughtfully before asking casually, 'I could do with a horse. Have you a mind to sell your mare?'

'My mare? No!' was the reply, 'Not for all Cumberland would I sell her. Her like is not to be found anywhere else in the country.'

Dickie agreed that she was a beautiful animal. 'I hear there are horse thieves in the neighbourhood,' he warned. 'I would recommend that you keep her close in case your stable should be empty some morning.'

'Stable? Her sleeps in no stable. I have no wife or children to keep me company. Her's my family. The mare stays in the hoose with myself, and it's music to my ears to hear her grinding her corn all night long.'

'Very wise,' commented Dickie, with a sinking heart. This was going to be difficult, but not impossible. He added, 'I hope you have a sound lock on your door.'

'I have that.' The farmer showed him the lock, which he stated was impossible to pick, and Dickie agreed with him; but inside, his good spirits were restored. He flashed his most dazzling smile and raised his cup.

'This is fine whisky, sir.'

The pair went on to finish the bottle before Dickie took his leave, at which point the old farmer was relaxed and finding it difficult to keep awake.

DICKIE OF KINGSWOOD

Once again, the damp hedgerows, full of spinning spiders, sheltered our villain until dead of night. Then, quiet as a ghost, he crept to the farmhouse and expertly picked the lock. Once inside, he found a few blankets which he laid on the floor between the horse and the door, and when he found that he was short of a blanket, he took the top one off the sleeping farmer's bed and placed that with the others. Gently, he untied the horse from its post and led it silently outside and away.

As he passed the field where the two oxen lay, he hesitated for a moment and smiled to himself; then he patted the mare's silky neck and continued on his way.

The old farmer woke in the morning shivering with cold. The door was open and his thick blanket was on the floor – and his mare had gone from her stall! He called for his servants and they searched the farm, but there was no trace of the thief or the horse. Eventually, anger and misery drove him inside to find the rest of his whisky.

Meanwhile, Dickie was galloping eastwards towards Starward Pele on the fleet-footed mare.

Three miles from home, on the fell above Haltwhistle, he came across a farmer tramping along on foot, looking weary and careworn. The man asked, 'Have ye seen a yoke of oxen on yer travels? White, and the finest beasts ye'll ever see. Them was stolen from me several days past.'

Dickie realised this was the farmer from Denton Burn. With a mischievous gleam in his eye, he told him that he had seen two fine beasts fitting the description, and he directed him to the farm in Lanercost.

'You ride a fine horse; will ye sell her?' asked the farmer. 'That scoundrel of a thief led me on a false chase almost as far north as Berwick before I realised I'd been hoodwinked, but my nag was lamed and I'm weary now of tramping on my blistered feet.'

A bargain was struck, and the farmer set off on the mare to find his oxen, leaving Dickie to walk the short distance to Starward Pele with a grin on his face and his pockets bulging with sovereigns.

When the farmer reached Lanercost, he spied his treasured beasts in the field. He hammered on the farmhouse door, which was eventually opened by a bleary-eyed old man who was swaying and blinking in the low autumn sunlight, and clutching a mug of whisky.

'Those are my cattle in the field. How did ye come by them?' barked the indignant stranger from Denton Burn.

The old man's confused gaze drifted unsteadily to the horse standing quietly by the man's side, and his face lit up like a beacon. 'My mare! Where did you find her?' He dropped the mug on the ground and staggered out to hug the horse's neck, which was foaming with sweat after being ridden so hard.

The two men swapped stories and it dawned on them that they had been duped by the same man. But they were so happy to be reunited with their animals that they soon forgot about the loss of the money that they had both given to Dickie, and they agreed to do an exchange with no hard feelings. This called for the breaking open of another bottle of whisky, and they could not help laughing heartily at the ludicrousness of the whole affair.

Dickie left Starward Pele for good after that, and he was never seen or heard of in the area again. One thing is fairly certain, though. His career as a thief would not have ended there. Many more people would have woken up in the morning, victims of the audacious rogue, Dickie of Kingswood.